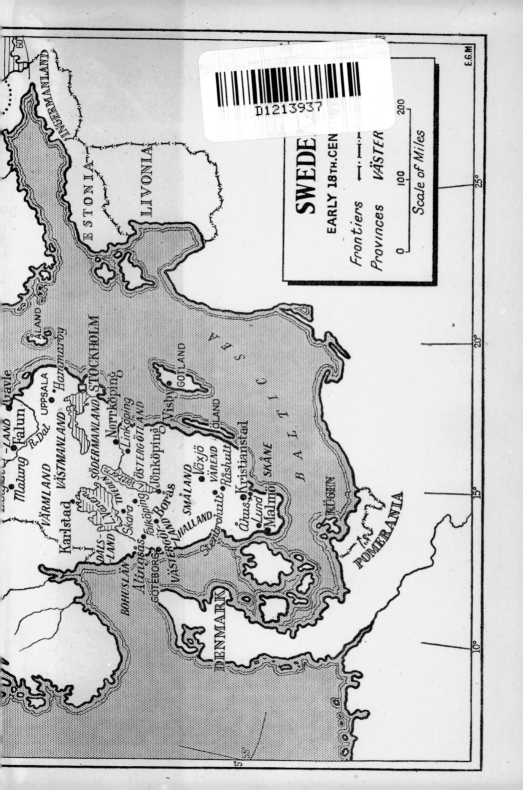

SWEDE

EARLY 18TH CEN

Frontiers

Provinces   VÄSTER

Scale of Miles

0   100   200

E.G.M

INGERMANLAND

ESTONIA

LIVONIA

ÅLAND

Hammarby

GÄVLE – LAND   Gävle
Malung   Falun   UPPSALA
R. Dal
VÄRMLAND   VÄSTMANLAND   SÖDERMANLAND   STOCKHOLM
Karlstad   Norrköping
DALS-   Linköping
LAND   Skara   ÖSTERGÖTLAND   GOTLAND
Alingsås   Jönköping   Visby
BOHUSLÄN   VÄSTERGÖT-   Borås   SMÅLAND   Växjö
GÖTEBORG   LAND   Folkköping   VÄREND   ÖLAND
HALLAND   Skenbrohult   Räshult
Åhus   Kristianstad
Lund   SKÅNE
Malmö

BALTIC

DENMARK

RÜGEN

POMERANIA

60

5

55

10°   15°   20°   25°

CARL LINNÆUS
From a portrait by A. Roslin

CARL LINNÆUS

by

KNUT HAGBERG

Translated from the Swedish by
ALAN BLAIR

JONATHAN CAPE
THIRTY BEDFORD SQUARE
LONDON

FIRST PUBLISHED 1952

This book is issued under the auspices of the Anglo-Swedish
Literary Foundation

Dewey Classification 925.8

PRINTED IN GREAT BRITAIN IN THE CITY OF OXFORD
AT THE ALDEN PRESS
BOUND BY A. W. BAIN & CO. LTD., LONDON

CONTENTS

ILLUSTRATIONS

PUBLISHER'S NOTE

The accurate rendering of Linnæus's individual style of writing has not been possible, and it has therefore been necessary to make slight adjustments for the purpose of easier reading. Whenever possible, the existing translations have been quoted verbatim.

CARL LINNÆUS

THE DECLINE AND FALL OF THE
SWEDISH EMPIRE

IN Dr. Samuel Johnson's *The Vanity of Human Wishes*, which may well be called one of the eighteenth century's noblest poems, there is a passage treating of Sweden and the great Swedish warrior king, Charles XII:

> On what foundation stands the warrior's pride,
> How just his hopes, let Swedish Charles decide;
> A frame of adamant, a soul of fire,
> No dangers fright him, and no labours tire;
> O'er love, o'er fear, extends his wide domain,
> Unconquer'd lord of pleasure and of pain;
> No joys to him pacific sceptres yield,
> War sounds the trump, he rushes to the field;
> Behold surrounding kings their pow'rs combine,
> And one capitulate, and one resign;
> Peace courts his hand, but spreads her charms in vain;
> 'Think nothing gain'd', he cries, 'till nought remain,
> On Moscow's walls till Gothic standards fly,
> And all be mine beneath the polar sky.'
> The march begins in military state,
> And nations on his eye suspended wait;
> Stern Famine guards the solitary coast,
> And Winter barricades the realm of Frost;
> He comes, nor want nor cold his course delay;
> Hide, blushing Glory, hide Pultowa's day;
> The vanquish'd hero leaves his broken bands,
> And shews his miseries in distant lands;
> Condemn'd a needy supplicant to wait,
> While ladies interpose, and slaves debate.
> But did not Chance at length her error mend?
> Did no subverted empire mark his end?
> Did rival monarchs give the fatal wound?
> Or hostile millions press him to the ground?
> His fall was destin'd to a barren strand,
> A petty fortress, and a dubious hand;

He left the name, at which the world grew pale,
To point a moral, or adorn a tale.

When *The Vanity of Human Wishes* was published, Dr.
Johnson could certainly count on his readers being able to
understand its allusions; through Voltaire's biography *Charles
XII* the destinies of the Swedish king were known all over civilized Europe. Nowadays Dr. Johnson's lines require an historical commentary to be fully comprehensible to English readers.

The Swedish empire of Charles XII was a mighty one.
Apart from present-day Sweden it included Finland, the
Baltic Provinces and westernmost Russia (Ingermanland),
where Leningrad now lies, and considerable portions of
northern Germany. Shortly after the young King Charles XII's
accession to the throne Sweden was attacked by a coalition
consisting of Denmark, Poland (with Saxony) and Russia.
King Charles's successes were in the beginning overwhelming.
Denmark was forced to capitulate without any appreciable
bloodshed, the Russians were defeated at Narva, Poland was
vanquished and its king dethroned. In 1707 Charles XII
marched forth from Saxony with a large and well-equipped
army; his goal was the capital of Russia, Moscow. But he was
overcome — as Napoleon was later on — by the Russian
winter; his soldiers froze to death in hundreds. At the Battle
of Poltava in 1709 the Swedish army could not be led by the
king, who had been wounded some days earlier, and the
Russians won a decisive victory. King Charles fled to Turkey,
where he incited the Sultan to take up arms against Russia.
Sweden's enemies were now increasing; the King of England
and the King of Prussia both joined the original coalition.
Safely home again, however, King Charles defended himself
vigorously, but in the autumn of 1718 he fell — probably
murdered — while besieging a fortress in Norway.

With him ended Sweden's supremacy as a Great Power.
Of her possessions round the Baltic she was allowed to keep
the greater part of Finland and certain portions of northern
Germany. Russia pushed forward to the Baltic. The war had
drained the strength of the Swedish people. Absolute mon-

archy was abolished and all power put into the hands of Parliament. Sweden was governed in more or less the same way as contemporary England; its German-born monarchs, who, like their English counterparts, could not speak the tongue of their adopted country, had a purely decorative place to fill. This period in Sweden's history has been called the Age of Liberty; political corruption was great, but the arts and sciences flourished. At the universities of Upsala and Lund and at the scientific institutions in Stockholm there were learned men who were the equals of the most brilliant in Europe.

Charles XII is also mentioned by Boswell. During a conversation in 1778 Dr. Johnson says:

Were Socrates and Charles the Twelfth of Sweden both present in any company, and Socrates to say, 'Follow me, and hear a lecture on philosophy'; and Charles, laying his hand on his sword, to say, 'Follow me, and dethrone the Czar'; a man would be ashamed to follow Socrates.

Of Carl Linnæus's Sweden during the Age of Liberty, however, it can be said that its best men were those who were more interested in philosophy than in war. An Englishman like Dr. Johnson, a Frenchman like Voltaire, could admire Charles XII without thinking it incumbent to deride the Swedish people, who had so long and loyally followed their warrior king. Thomas Carlyle judges more harshly. In the first volume of his great work, *The History of Friedrich II of Prussia, called Frederick the Great,* a work which with English eloquence convinced Germany that Prussia was God's nation elect, Carlyle launches out against Sweden and the Swedes. He tells how his beloved Prussians undertook God's mission by laying siege to the town of Stralsund, a Swedish town then and long afterwards, and in magnificent style he takes the opportunity of giving a picture of 'the decline and fall of the Swedish empire':

Poor Charles, there had been no sleep for him that night, and little for very many nights: 'on getting to horse, on the shore at Stralsund, he fainted repeatedly; fell out of one faint into another; but such was his rage, he always recovered himself, and got on horseback again' (Buchholz, i, 36). Poor Charles: a bit of right royal Swedish-German stuff, after his kind; and tragically ill bestead now at last! This is his exit he is now making, — still in a consistent manner. It is fifteen years now since he waded ashore at Copenhagen, and first heard the bullets whistle round him. Since which time, what a course has he run; crashing athwart all manner of ranked armies, diplomatic combinations, right onward, like a cannon-ball; tearing off many solemn wigs in those Northern parts, and scattering them upon the winds, — even as he did his own full-bottom wig, impatiently, on that first day at Copenhagen, finding it unfurthersome for actual business in battle.

In about a month hence, the last important hornwork is forced; Charles, himself seen fiercely fighting on the place, is swept back from his last hornwork; and the general storm, now altogether irresistible, is evidently at hand. On entreaty from his followers, entreaty often renewed, with tears even (it is said) and on bended knees, Charles at last consents to go. He left no orders for surrender; would not name the word; 'left only ambiguous vague orders'. But on the 19th December, 1715, he does actually depart; gets on board a little boat, towards a Swedish frigate, which is lying above a mile out; the whole road to which, between Rügen and the mainland, is now solid ice, and has to be cut as he proceeds. This slow operation, which lasted all day, was visible, and its meaning well known, in the besiegers' lines. The King of Denmark saw it; and brought a battery to bear upon it; his thought had always been, that Charles should be captured or killed in Stralsund, and not allowed to get away. Friedrich Wilhelm was of quite another mind, and had even used secret influences to that effect; eager that Charles should escape. It is said, he remonstrated very passionately with the Danish King and this battery of his; nay, some add, since remonstrances did not avail, and the battery still threatened to fire, Friedrich Wilhelm drew up a Prussian regiment or two at the muzzles of it, and said, You shall shoot us first, then. Which is a pleasant myth at least; and symbolical of what the reality was.

Charles reached his frigate about nightfall, but made little way from the place, owing to defect of wind. They say, he

even heard the chamade beating in Stralsund next day, and
that a Danish frigate had nearly taken him; both which
statements are perhaps also a little mythical. Certain only that
he vanished at this point into Scandinavia; and general Europe
never saw him more. Vanished into a cloud of untenable
schemes, guided by Alberoni, Baron Görtz and others; wild
schemes, financial, diplomatic, warlike, nothing not chimerical
in them but his own unquenchable real energy;— and found
his death (by assassination, as appears) in the trenches of
Frederickshall, among the Norway Hills, one winter night,
three years hence. Assassination instigated by the Swedish
Official Persons, it is thought. The bullet passed through both
his temples; he had clapt his hand upon the hilt of his sword,
and was found leant against the parapet, in that attitude,—
gone upon a long march now. So vanished Charles Twelfth;
the distressed Official Persons and Nobility exploding upon
him in that rather damnable way,— anxious to slip their
muzzles at any cost whatever. A man of antique character;
true as a child, simple, even bashful, and of a strength and
valour rarely exampled among men. Open-hearted Antique
populations would have much worshipped such an Appearance;— Voltaire, too, for the artificial Moderns, has made a
myth of him, of another type; one of those impossible cast-iron
gentlemen, heroically mad, such as they show in the Play-
houses, pleasant but not profitable, to an undiscerning Public.
The last of the Swedish Kings died in this way; and the
unmuzzled Official Persons have not made much of kinging
it in his stead. Charles died; and, as we may say, took the life
of Sweden along with him; for it has never shone among the
Nations since, or been much worth mentioning, except for its
misfortunes, spasmodic impotences and unwisdoms.

Poor Sweden—too old, according to Carlyle, to be mentioned
among the vigorous and industrious peoples of Europe, with
Bismarck's Prussia at the head. But the Swedes and their
rulers during the eighteenth century thought, moved, and had
their being more in the manner of Voltaire than of Thomas
Carlyle. And Sweden managed, in spite of everything, to
produce men whose lives and work cannot in all fairness be
dismissed as 'spasmodic impotences and unwisdoms'.

Charles XII and Charles Linnæus have become the most renowned of all Swedes.

When Linnæus was christened in the spring of 1707 and named after the king, Sweden was the most powerful country in Europe. Her traditional ally, the France of Louis XIV, had been badly maimed by hostile forces led by the Duke of Marlborough. An English reader can best gain an impression of Sweden's position at that time on the chessboard of power politics by reading the chapter on Marlborough and Charles XII in the third volume of Winston Churchill's *Life of Marlborough*. The Sweden in which Linnæus grew up, lived, and died, however, had changed from Charles XII's mighty empire to but a second-class power. Its frontiers stretched across wide areas, but they were sparsely populated and the kingdom's economic and military resources were of little account.

When Linnæus was young, Sweden, together with Finland, had about 2,000,000 inhabitants. The population of England and Wales at that time was estimated at about 5,500,000; that of France at approximately 20,000,000. Sweden and Finland were then, as now, mostly covered by vast forests, but in the plains the cultivation was old and round the medieval cathedrals there existed venerable seats of learning. Besides the university towns of Upsala and Lund — Sweden's equivalents of Oxford and Cambridge — there were learned schools, rightly held in high esteem, in Västerås and Strängnäs, Skara, Linköping and Växjö. Here were studied not only the classical languages and the dogmatics of the Swedish state church, but also natural science. In Växjö, where Linnæus went to school, the teachers could, despite scant pay and evil times, keep abreast of educational literature from abroad.

Sweden as a Great Power had been founded by Gustavus Adolphus and was strictly Lutheran. It had grown strong in the struggle against the Catholic powers in Germany. The fact that it was intimately allied to Catholic France made no difference. The language of the learned was Latin; in aristocratic circles French was spoken. But towards the end of the seventeenth century and in the beginning of the eighteenth century a new influence made itself felt. Young Swedes journeyed abroad in increasing numbers, especially to London; England's political ideas and above all modern English natural science affected Swedish culture to an ever greater degree.

The spirit of the new natural science in England has been brilliantly summed up by Macaulay:

The attention of speculative men had been, for the first time, directed to the important subject of sanitary police. The great plague of 1665 induced them to consider with care the defective architecture, draining, and ventilation of the capital. The great fire of 1666 afforded an opportunity for effecting extensive improvements. The whole matter was diligently examined by the Royal Society; and to the suggestions of that body must be partly attributed the changes which, though far short of what the public welfare required, yet made a wide difference between the new and the old London, and probably put a final close to the ravages of pestilence in our country. At the same time one of the founders of the Society, Sir William Petty, created the science of political arithmetic, the humble but indispensable handmaid of political philosophy. No kingdom of nature was left unexplored. To that period belong the chemical discoveries of Boyle, and the earliest botanical researches of Sloane. It was then that Ray made a new classification of birds and fishes, and that the attention of Woodward was first drawn towards fossils and shells. One after another phantoms which had haunted the world through ages of darkness fled before the light. Astrology and alchymy became jests. Soon there was scarcely a county in which some of the Quorum did not smile contemptuously when an old woman was brought before them for riding on broomsticks or giving cattle the murrain. But it was in those noblest and most arduous departments of knowledge in which induction and mathematical demonstration co-operate for the discovery of truth, that the English genius won in that age the most memorable triumphs. John Wallis placed the whole system of statics on a new foundation. Edmund Halley investigated the properties of the atmosphere, the ebb and flow of the sea, the laws of magnetism, and the course of the comets; nor did he shrink from toil, peril, and exile in the cause of science. While he, on the rock of Saint Helena, mapped the constellations of the southern hemisphere, our national observatory was rising at Greenwich; and John Flamstead, the first Astronomer Royal, was commencing that long series of observations which is never mentioned without respect and gratitude in any part of the globe. But the glory of these men, eminent as they were, is cast into the shade by the transcendent lustre of one immortal name. In Isaac Newton two kinds of intellectual power, which have little in common, and which are not often found together in a very high degree of vigour, but which nevertheless are equally necessary in the most sublime departments of physics, were united as they have never been united before or since. There may have been minds as happily constituted as his for the cultivation of pure mathematical science: there may have been minds as happily constituted for the cultivation of science purely experimental: but in no other mind have the demonstrative faculty and the inductive faculty coexisted in such supreme excellence and perfect harmony.

The famous natural scientist and religious philosopher Emanuel Swedenborg — himself related to Linnæus — was one of the many who received their decisive youthful impressions in England, and in letters to Swedish relatives he liked to use the English language. But neither in Sweden nor in England did this interest in natural science imply a breach with ancestral faith.

The Swedish countryside with its flowery meadows and pleasant groves of oak and hazel encompassed by fir-forests; the Swedish Lutheran church's order of divine service, in many ways like that of the Church of England, and the daily Bible-reading; the humanistic education, which chiefly involved an assiduous study of Latin poets and prose writers; and finally the stimulus of new scientific discoveries in England — these were the four main factors that determined the development of the Swedish genius, Carl Linnæus.

CHAPTER I

CURRICULUM VITÆ

CARL LINNÆUS was born on May 23rd
(Old Style: May 13th) in the year 1707. His father,
Nils Linnæus, was perpetual curate of Råshult, and his
mother, Christina Brodersonia, was the daughter of the vicar
of the adjacent village, Stenbrohult. His father came of
peasant stock; the young mother belonged to a well-born
clerical family. Shortly after his son's birth Nils Linnæus
succeeded his father-in-law as vicar of Stenbrohult.

Carl Linnæus's childhood home was in the southernmost
part of the province of Småland, near the border of Skåne. It
is a kindly and beautiful part of the country, rich in flowers.
These the boy learned to love from the very cradle. His father
had a good knowledge of botany and round the vicarage he
laid out a botanical garden which, judged by the standards of
the age, was considerable. The future natural scientist could
hardly have grown up under more fortunate conditions.

The nearest city was Växjö, with bishop, cathedral, and a
school of high repute at which the principal subjects were the
classical languages and divinity. Carl Linnæus began his
studies at this school in 1716, and there he learned to write and
speak Latin as his mother tongue. But in the higher forms
natural science was also taught, and Linnæus's teacher in that
subject, Dr. Rothman, was a learned scientist who encouraged
his pupil to read and study the most outstanding scientific
works of the age, especially on botany.

After studying for a year at the South-Swedish university of
Lund, Linnæus went in 1728 to the university of Upsala,
where he soon aroused the attention of the professors. As
early as 1730 he was installed as lecturer and demonstrator at
the university's botanical garden.

Two years later he received a grant for the undertaking of

CARL LINNÆUS

an extensive scientific journey to Lappland. It was a strenuous but particularly profitable one; and Linnæus recounted his remarkable finds and observations in *Flora Lapponica*, written in Latin and published in Amsterdam in 1737; the Swedish diary of his journey, however, was not published until 1811, and then in London in an English translation by J. E. Smith, president of the Linnean Society, under the title of *A Tour in Lapland*.

The young scientist's name began to be known. In 1733 he was asked to lecture on geology at Upsala; in 1734, on the initiative of the Governor of Dalarna, he undertook a botanical, zoological, and geological tour of exploration through this province. During this journey he got to know Sara Lisa, the daughter of a wealthy doctor, Johan Moræus, and became engaged to her.

His immediate goal then was to acquire the degree of doctor of medicine and to find a publisher for his unpublished works. His monetary resources were small, but he knew he had something of value to give the world and experience had taught him that he easily gained patrons and friends.

In 1735, therefore, he set out for Holland, where he took his medical degree at Hardewijk. From there he went to Leiden, where he immediately found a fatherly friend in the great Dutch natural scientist and doctor, Boerhaave. Here Linnæus swiftly won fame in the world of learning with his work *Systema Naturæ*, in which he gave an account of his revolutionary ideas concerning the systematism of the animal, vegetable, and mineral kingdoms. Through Boerhaave he became acquainted with the rich banker, Clifford, with whom he received employment on dazzling terms as superintendent of Clifford's magnificent zoological and botanical garden at Hartecamp.

In Holland Linnæus published a whole list of epoch-making works, among which may be mentioned *Flora Lapponica*, *Genera Plantarum*, *Critica Botanica*; an admirable English translation by Sir Arthur Hort of the last-named work was published by The Ray Society in 1938.

In 1736 Linnæus had the chance of visiting England; he has spoken of this in his *Autobiographical Memoranda*:

In 1736 Linnæus went to England at the expense of Mr. Clifford. Here he not only viewed the Gardens of Chelsea and Oxford, but also procured therefrom the most rare plants, which had come in and had still not been described, and made himself acquainted with the learned men who were there. In Oxford Linnæus was most politely received by Doctor Shaw, who had travelled in Barbary and counted himself a disciple of Linnæus, in that he had read his *Systema* with such great pleasure. The learned botanist Dillenius at first received Linnæus with scorn, as he considered that the *Genera* of Linnæus, which he had had sent over from Holland half printed, were written in opposition to him, but subsequently detained Linnæus for months on end, without leaving him in peace for one hour of the day, and finally let him go with tears and kisses, having first begged him to live and die with him, the professor's salary being sufficient for them both.

After visiting France as well, Linnæus left Holland in 1738 and returned to Sweden, already a famous man at the age of thirty-one. In Stockholm he practised as a doctor with great success; of especial significance was his new method for the curing of venereal diseases. After numerous struggles for preferment he was made professor of medicine and natural history at Upsala, where he continued to work for the remainder of his life.

His subjects were comprehensive: he lectured on zoology, botany, geology, practical medicine, and hygiene. The remarkable thing is that his achievements in all these fields were epoch-making. His literary production was of astonishing dimensions, embracing a large number of enormous works and hundreds of smaller theses in Latin and Swedish, all stamped with the author's scientific genius.

One or two of the more important ones have these titles: *Flora Svecica*, 1745; *Fauna Svecica*, 1746; *Curiositas Naturalis*, 1748; *Materia Medica*, 1749; *Philosophia Botanica*, 1751; *Species Plantarum*, 1753; *Politia Naturæ*, 1760. His *Systema*

Naturæ grew to be a mammoth work; especially important is the tenth edition, the first volume of which was brought out in a facsimile edition by the British Museum in 1939.

Linnæus was by no means merely a scientist. He was one of Sweden's greatest writers, a poet and a thinker. By order of Parliament he journeyed through the Swedish provinces — Öland and Gotland in 1741, Västergötland in 1746 and Skåne in 1749 — and his descriptions of these journeys are counted among the finest writing in Swedish literature. His language at times has a poetic quality, the brilliance of which time has not managed to dim. But there were also dark streaks in his make-up, for his was a very complex nature.

In 1758 he bought a country estate at Hammarby, outside Upsala. This was where he preferred to live, and it has now been restored to its original state.

Honours were heaped upon him. He was made royal physician (*arkiater*) and a member of most of the learned academies and societies in Europe. In 1762 he was ennobled and received the name von Linné.

Pupils flocked to his lectures at Upsala from all corners of Europe, and many of these pupils later made botanical exploration tours to far-off lands, to Palestine and Arabia, to North America and Brazil, to South Africa and Japan. One of them, D. C. Solander, settled in England and later accompanied Cook on his voyage round the world, 1768-71. Rare plants from all over the world were sent to Upsala and Hammarby.

By his wife, Sara, whom he married in 1739, Linnæus had two sons, one dying when three years old, and four daughters. The surviving son, Carl von Linné the younger, succeeded his father as professor at Upsala but only outlived him by five years. He was an eminent botanist, but of lesser degree than his great father. He died unmarried, but through two of his sisters there are numerous Swedes now living who can claim descent from Carl Linnæus.

In 1774 Linnæus, or von Linné as he had now become, was seized by a stroke, his faculties failed, and his final years were sombre.

In 1778 death came to set him free. On January 22nd, a dark and gloomy evening, by the light of lanterns and blazing torches and to the tolling of the bells, the mortal remains of Carl Linnæus were borne in a great procession to the tomb in Upsala Cathedral. It was a long road in time and achievement from the spring morning in Stenbrohult when he first saw the light of day. In the autumn of 1778 the Swedish king, Gustav III, said in his speech from the throne to Parliament:

I have lost a man who has done honour to his country as a loyal subject, as well as being renowned throughout the world.

CHAPTER II

STENBROHULT

ON April 29th, 1707 (Old Style) Charles, by the grace of God King of Sweden, of the Goths and the Wends, Grand Duke of Finland, Duke of Skåne, Estonia, Livonia, Karelia, Bremen, Verden, Stettin, Pommerania, Kashubia and Wenden, Prince of Rügen, Lord of Ingermanland and Wismar, likewise Count Palatine of the Rhine in Bavaria, Duke of Jülich, Cleve and Berg, from the Swedish army camp in Saxony wrote a letter to his sister, the *durchleuchtigste* Princess Ulrika Eleonora. Lieutenant-General Count Knut Posse, in his capacity of newly appointed Privy Councillor and Governor-General, was to set out from Altranstädt for Stockholm, and this being so the King could not, in his own words:

neglect this opportunity of Posse's leaving here to send a few lines in great haste and pay my humble and obedient respects to my very dearest Sister, and I beg *mon cœur* constantly to preserve her precious favour towards me and not to weary of overlooking my prolonged negligence, in that I have so often and so long been constrained to omit paying my due respects, being prevented from writing by sundry hindrances and then, being a very unskilled writer, finding it a great effort to write.

The letter continues with French compliments, translated verbatim into clumsy Swedish, which have the supreme quality of concealing all sense under a baroque magniloquence. And with the letter in his pocket Count Posse journeyed northwards.

Let us accompany the traveller in imagination. In keeping with his rank he rode in a four-horse coach with outrider and baggage-coach, furnished with a diplomatic passport. It is likely that in order to avoid an uncertain crossing of the Baltic he took the road through Denmark, then a humbled and very meek neighbour state of the Great Power, Sweden. Provided that respectful Danish county barons did not retard his Lordship's journey with banquets, he should, by Sunday, May 12th, have got as far as just beyond the border of Småland.

The scent of the Swedish springtime flowers would doubtless penetrate right into the coach, and at each change of horses the wrangling of the lackeys with the ostlers would be drowned by a jubilant chorus of birds. But Knut Posse had graver matters to consider as, fatigued by the jolting of the coach, he took a pinch of snuff. He was a great and powerful man, and the capital city he was now to administer as Governor-General was the focal point of a kingdom which, after France and England, was the strongest in Europe. At the head of a formidable army its king was now about to march forth and make a radical change in the map of Eastern Europe. But as Count Posse's coach climbed towards the uplands of Småland it may perhaps have occurred to its occupant that this land, with its boundless expanse of lakes and forests, was less fitted to give swift delivery of ready-equipped regiments than the principalities of the German lowlands. At all events, the Privy Council, of which Posse was now a member, acted as though such were its conviction.

The coach wound its way through the Värend countryside over the hilly, stony roads. When would the King really learn to understand the claims and requirements of the realm? The Muscovite was far into Ingermanland. The kingdom's economic resources would soon be exhausted. But the invincible army, equipped as never before, now had its word to say.

In this far-flung land it could not be expected even of a prospective Privy Councillor to remember the innumerable parishes. But on his way home he inquired for the nearest country seats whose names reminded him of comrades-in-arms or suggested future fellow Councillors. If on the night of May 12th the horses of Count Posse's coach were changed in the vicinity of Stenbrohult church, it is conceivable that the traveller had decided to have a good sleep at Möckelnsnäs, where Mr. Justice Cederhielm resided when his official duties as sheriff did not detain him elsewhere.

That same night a male child was born in the nearby vicarage of Råshult.

Whether the sun on the morning of May 13th shone down on Count Posse's coach on its way north from Stenbrohult is uncertain; for the journey may, as mentioned, have taken quite a different course. But it did shine down on a kingdom which, in growing might and ascendancy, saw its last summer as a Great Power. And it illuminated a landscape which in its wonderful richness, beauty, and lush verdure has, more than any other part of the Swedish countryside, proved capable of withstanding those forces which, since the beginning of the eighteenth century, have so fundamentally altered the Swedish scene. The mighty kingdom was suffering from political dropsy in its last stages, but the meadows of Stenbrohult have endured.

* * *

Carl Linnæus has given the clearest and most concise description of his native countryside in the chapter on the natural history of Småland which was included in the *Historical Account of Småland* published in 1770. It is also noteworthy that most of what he depicts there still holds good today. But, generally speaking, the ditching of bog-land, forestry, and the cultivation of clover have fashioned a Swedish landscape which has but little similarity with that of our fathers. Gone are the waterlogged fields, the wildflower-covered slopes, the oak woods where dark, lean pigs grubbed for acorns, the shaggy goats under their turf roofs, the dense hazel thickets whose leaves were gathered as fodder for small, matted cobs and undersized cows with long narrow snouts. They are all gone, together with the responsibilities of our dominion on the other side of the Baltic.

But near Stenbrohult, especially at Möckelnsnäs, the ancient Germanic vegetation still lingers, the oak woods that Cæsar grappled with and Tacitus described. Surrounded by fir forests, which towards the south become intrusive, it stands as a relic from a time when the whole Scandinavian conception of life was built up in harmony with the budding, the bursting into leaf, the flowering and the withering of the great deciduous trees. It is a Shakespearean landscape, with mighty oaks, hornbeams, maples, ashes, dense undergrowth, wildflowers that Linnæus especially loved: globe-flowers and bachelor's buttons.

Also, two hundred years ago this countryside was very individual, not to say unique. It had all the characteristics of the idyllic landscape of Lake Mälaren but with a few Southern Swedish elements — particularly the beech trees; the resemblance to Windsor Park, however, in this favoured region was due not to art but to nature. So much has been written about Linnæus's fondness for the artificial arable landscape; it was in fact his native countryside he held dear. It is difficult to depict its contours and peculiarities in words. From the summit of Taxås the leafy isles of Lake Möckeln gleam like green frigates; the austere fir-forest assigns a limit to the lucent idyll. Below Stenbrohult church the waves ripple in the inlet of the lake where the alder boughs shelter the water-lilies in their mud-bemingled peace. But the summer flowers flaunt their beauty on the dry upland pastures, and from the pine-capped ridges issue stretches of juniper and heather. Perhaps one can most graphically describe the present picture by recalling its physical history. There are still relics here and there in Sweden from the great climatic deterioration of the bronze age; on southern slopes in Jämtland hazel can be found, and on the high ground that slopes down towards Skåne the temperate age has left behind a much more lush memento, *Flora Stenbrohultiensis*, comprising most of the beauty of the Swedish natural scene, the coolness of the North and the luxuriance of Central Europe.

In two hundred years buildings have completely changed, as well as the livestock and the forest boundaries. The fields too, for flax and hops have gone and wheat has come in their stead; oats and rye had fewer ears of yore; cornflowers vied in profusion with knapweed where now the crops are compact, and the clover fields gleamed with daisies. But it is through the sense of hearing rather than of sight that one realizes the difference between the Stenbrohult of today and the Stenbrohult familiar to Linnæus.

Of the spring in his native countryside Linnæus wrote that with all the birds it sounded like paradise. The level of the water in Lake Möckeln was a few yards higher then than it is now, the marshes away towards Såganäs filled the now drained clover-fields with the scent of bog-myrtle, and the gun had not yet caused any appreciable decrease in the bird life. When in 1735 the young Linnæus on his way to the south and its splendour, on the road to recognition and honour, reined in his shaggy cob just after the painful leave-taking of home and was reminded of paradise — not lost but regained — by the song of birds, what was it he listened to? That is a question which must be answered if we are to understand him. He heard the throstle, the song-thrush, which he loved and of which he said that it put the nightingale to shame; he heard the different species of *Sylvia*, perhaps even the icterine warbler and the barred warbler, though these master-musicians were rather late in penetrating up towards Stenbrohult. But he also heard the liquid cry of the curlew, the common snipe drum across the meadows, and the quail's triple note; he may even have strained his ears for the booming of the bittern from across the marsh. He listened to an evensong from a paradise which for us is closed and gone for ever.

If one rows today across Möckeln on an evening in early summer, one is apt to try to imagine the changes which have occurred there since Linnæus's time. Despite the drop in the water-level the plant life is mainly the same. The osprey circles in wide rings, and the kite too is left. The diver gives its incessant high call and the raven croaks, betokening primitive Gothic superstition; but the didapper calling in its evening flight is a newcomer; Linnæus was not well acquainted with it, as is apparent from the descriptions of his travels and lectures on zoology. Another newcomer is the heron, which is now numerous round Möckeln. But Linnæus tells that in the migrating season the goosander was found in such numbers in Möckeln that people on the shore had only to await the time when the birds were hunting to catch fish in hundreds as they were driven terrified into the inlets. This is no longer the case, although goosander and garrot still occur; even the mallard has decreased.

With these known facts in mind, it is easy to conjure up in one's imagination the sparkle of the waves on the lake shore on May 13th, 1707 — according to our chronology May 23rd. It is an Elysian morning. The call of the quail wakes the grey-speckled swine in the oak woods below Taxås. A bittern booms. A wryneck screeches. Bird song rises from leafy woods wet with dew. Outside the curate's house on the slope leading from the wood, where the apple trees are in bloom above a well-manured kitchen garden and where lilies-of-the-valley diffuse their fragrance from the ditch, the roller, Queen Christina's bird, in its glittering array of feathers, is hopping about among the oaks, and through leaded panes eyes filled with tears of exhaustion look out towards the dawn. For a young woman has been delivered of her first-born and the night has been heavy. A pewter goblet with strong, heavy ale goes the rounds.

And Knut Posse's coach jolts northwards with a letter from King Charles.

*   *   *

Thanks to the fertile brain and conscientiousness of Gotthard Virdestam, a scientist who was also vicar of Älmhult and who died all too young, we know quite a lot about Stenbrohult's history. The church was first mentioned in the will, made in the year 1337, of a knight — Bengt Tukesson, Lord of Möckelnsnäs. One can visualize the greatly respected peasant population of the district from Hyltén-Cavallius's classical work *Värend and its Inhabitants*; but it is only through certain racial attributes that one can associate Linnæus with the peasants of Värend. A writer on Swedish provincial characteristics has tried to draw a distinction between two ancient Småland types:

On the one hand we have a tall, blond race of a marked Germanic type. It is the kind of people one meets chiefly in the agricultural district of Värend. The women are often of tall stature, the lower part of the body being long and the upper part leaning slightly forward; they are unusually dolichocephalic, and often have beautiful, finely-cut features.

And of the second type the author says:

The most noticeable Småland type is of quite another species, one is almost tempted to say of quite another race: shorter of stature and less dolichocephalic, often darker and more lively, not seldom talkative and having a pronounced nervous energy.

That these descriptions are reliable and to the point is clearly apparent from the fact that they fit like a glove the two people whose offspring was Carl Linnæus.

One need only look at the frequently reproduced portraits. Christina Brodersonia, painted as a seventeen-year-old bride, has clear-cut features which are very aristocratic, and something of the 'old school' about her noble bearing. Compare with this the picture of Nils Linnæus, a small, brown-eyed man with alert and restless glance. Two streams of the Småland national characteristics have thus been blended in our country's greatest scientific genius.

Carl Linnæus's maternal grandfather and great-grandfather were vicars of Stenbrohult and were extensively related to the surrounding gentry. But Nils Linnæus was only the son of a well-to-do farmer. Among his memoranda about his family there is one remark that is worthy of note:

Anno 1702, [he tells us] on 9th Julius, I journeyed across to Denmark by way of Helsingör, on the 11th to Copenhagen. I had then intended going to Holland, but as I found I had but scant fortune I crossed on 1st Septembris over to Skåne.

Several inferences can be drawn from this. When a Småland country student in Lund decides in the summer of 1702 to journey to Holland, he must first and foremost be quite well off. Secondly he must have a burning desire to study. For a journey

to Holland was hazardous when the curtain had just risen on the
first act of the great northern war. One can also determine the
nature of the young student's avidity for knowledge. Why did
he wish to go to Holland in particular? He was to study for
the Church, and Swedish bishops in embryo were hatched out
at orthodox universities in Germany. In heretical Holland — a
Calvinist at that time was even more dangerous for the
Lutherans than a Catholic — instruction was given in medicine
and anatomy. That was the longed for goal of Nils Linnæus.
It is really rather strange that no one has seen that the son's
predilections were inherited from his father.

When during the autumn term of 1702 it became increasingly evident that peace was out of the question, that
people were to be coerced and money extorted, none knew as
yet how thoroughly, and that all thought of scholarship was a
fool's paradise as long as Poland's affairs were at stake, Nils
Linnæus returned to Stenbrohult and won the highest prize
then open to him — the vicar of Stenbrohult's young and
beautiful daughter and the curate's dwelling-house at Råshult.

The curacy was soon changed for the benefice of Stenbrohult by the father-in-law's decease, for through the gentry at
Möckelnsnäs the ear of King Charles was gained and he was
easily convinced that the family succession was more important
than the sheaves of appeals lodged by rivals concerning their
ecclesiastical merits. And fortunately we know quite a lot
about the merits of Nils Linnæus's preaching and work.

It is true that no one has been able to say of him with the
same conviction as was said of his son and successor — Carl
Linnæus's brother Samuel — that he was a good economist, for
these laudatory words at that time would not only have meant
that the vicar kept his own accounts in order but the county's
too. One must consider that even though in those days the
vicar belonged to a different class from the farmers, he was
himself the 'county economist', and for the vicar to deserve the
epithet 'good economist' he would be expected to devise
financial expedients for the benefit of the parish. From what
we now know of him through his own memoranda, his sons'

writings and the brief diocesan annals, Nils Linnæus seems to have been a preacher of the Word who gained his ends more by gentleness and understanding than by severe and forthright preaching.

What his Church's outward guise meant to him is apparent from the gallery railing from Stenbrohult preserved in Lund; it lay close to his heart to deck in fine array the Lord's temple in Stenbrohult, which had been violated during Charles XI's war. But his dream of going to Holland kept a firm hold on him, and in the soft, fertile ground just south of the church, hard by Möckeln, sheltered from the winds and watched over by the western sun, he fashioned a Holland in miniature. Its appearance is evident from Carl Linnæus's work *Adonis Stenbrohultiensis*, but the idyllic spot is so well described by Virdestam that it is as well to leave his account unchanged:

It was not the utilitarian aspect [Virdestam writes] that was the driving power in Linnæus's interest in his garden; he was inspired by a tender love of collecting in which the scientific element was not entirely lacking. 'He esteemed', writes Samuel Linnæus, 'the smallest and most insignificant plant as highly as the fairest sweet-smelling flower, though such were not wanting either in the garden during his lifetime; he always wished for more species than he had.' The garden therefore contained a rich variety of plants, which were useful or purely ornamental, as well as mere curiosities, which were probably cultivated in hot-beds or greenhouses. Of fruit and berries there were to be found several kinds of apples, pears, plums, cherries, gooseberries, currants, raspberries and strawberries. The kitchen garden doubtless made the vicarage kitchen the one best supplied with vegetables in Småland; in the catalogue we find, amongst others, carrots, turnips, artichokes, beetroot, radishes, horse-radish, several kinds of cabbage, beans, peas and onions, asparagus, lettuce, spinach, cucumbers, pumpkins, parsley, dill, thyme, sweet marjoram, chervil, celery, mustard, and wormwood. Special rarities were mulberry-trees, small fig-trees, dwarf-almonds, grey hyssop and truffles, i.e. potatoes, also possibly one or two other plants with indications of foreign origin, such as Turkish wheat,

Roman nettles and Lombardy nuts. No less numerous were the ornamental plants; they too were Linnæus's especial favourites. Of these there were tulips and violets, daffodils and white narcissus, fritillaries and peonies, aconites, larkspurs and columbines, several kinds of lilies, carnations, poppies, lupins and roses, nasturtiums, marigolds and daisies, salvia and balm, southernwood and lavender, snowballs and jasmine, to say nothing of many others. It is easy to imagine a mid-summer's day in this garden as being a glorious experience; the shady trees, the bright, sweet-smelling flowers, the hum of bees, the singing of birds and the cooing of doves, and last but not least the lovely view across the crystal-clear inlet of the lake towards the smiling shore of Möckelnsnäs, verdure-clad and fair, all this must have given a spectator endowed with a love of nature the impression of abiding in a blissful paradise of loveliness and peace.

With Bible and hymn-book in front of him on the pulpit in a church that was cheerless despite all the vivid pictures of the holy apostles, it was imperative for Nils Linnæus to show that his toil and delight in his garden was work acceptable in the eyes of the Lord. One thing he as a preacher was spared: he did not have to comment on Swedish politics. The farmers who listened to him had far too much to do with the stubborn soil from which in a righteous way they were to gain their bread, with witchcraft and sorcery that probably gave them an illusion of help, with thoughts of death, heaven, and hell, with whose realities they were soon to be confronted, to have time to wag their tongues or to interest themselves in the diversions of the King and the gentlemen of Stockholm. They knew that not even the worst tax impositions or levying of men could hit them one tithe so hard as a disastrous harvest. What they wished to hear from the pulpit were words and promises concerning the year's crops and next winter's snow conditions: accompanied by incantations that might accord their relations peace in their graves.

It has been said that Linnæus was influenced in his style by Arndt's form of preaching, and that Arndt's love of nature most likely had a great influence on both Linnæus and Bell-man. But in my opinion one can go much further and say that the general propensity in eighteenth-century Sweden to confuse theology and natural science was due in no small measure to the fact that Arndt's book of family sermons had been read in middle-class homes and rectories since the early seventeenth century, and had been assiduously used by preachers in the pulpit.

To assert flatly that Arndt's *The True Christianity* is an expression of so-called natural theology would be quite wrong. The book deals with all aspects of Christian life, and its historical significance is that it has given life and intensity to a protestantism benumbed by orthodoxy. But it also goes without saying that the great book, like the Bible, was read by different people in different ways. What one person liked to linger over the other might pass by. And quite considerable excerpts from Arndt's *The True Christianity* can be read as a fair exposition of the text on which 'natural theologians' subsequently used to preach.

This is particularly true of the fourth book, *Liber Naturæ,* which treats of God's creation. For the convenience of the reader I am not going to quote here a seventeenth-century edition but a nineteenth-century version, the meaning being clearer in the later language.

Arndt speaks of how one should admire and meditate on God's work on the fifth day of creation:

As is now said of the great waters, that they are branches and subdivisions of the element of water, so can one under-stand the same of metals, of minerals, of gold, silver, copper, iron, tin, lead and of precious stones, emeralds, sapphires, corals, garnets, etc. Likewise of salts, potash, vitriol. Further-more of springs, sour, sweet, cold, warm, etc. Also of mountain precipices and ravines and the like: the diffusion of them all over the entire earth comes from the element of water. And they all have their seed, their root, and stem in water. And can it otherwise be understood than that just as manifold trees of various kinds grow up out of the earth, having each its own fruit, so is it with the element of water: it forces its trees and metallic fruits into the crevices and veins of the earth; coagulation and hardening takes place, and a metallic or mineral tree is born, spreading out its branches still further in the earth, so that they may often extend for twenty, forty, sixty or more miles. When the fruit has ripened and fallen off, that same tree withers and dies of itself, and so the mines decay, die out and are consumed, which is the end of all creatures. A new one arises, however, in another place, and thus has the sole and wise Creator ordained everything to its appointed time and end.

This may very well be read by us with attention as an interesting example of the natural philosophy of the Renaissance. But one should remember that this and similar excerpts from Arndt were in no way studied as information concerning the nature of metals, but as edification, as the gospel itself. It was spoken from the pulpit and listened to with heads bowed in reverence.

When Arndt speaks of the fish only a blind man could contest that there was a very great similarity between his preaching and that of a theologian of the 1780s, Dean Wåhlin. Arndt writes:

It is exceedingly wondrous that the great multitude of fish comes forth out of the deep at a certain time and shows itself as a flock of sheep, and gives itself into the hands of men and offers itself as food. Why, the sea is one large, wondrous larder of God, from which He feeds the greater part of the world, yea, from which come the most precious fruits and spices. Therefrom come the pearls, the agates, the amber, the corals, as Ovid says:

Sic et Coralium, quum primum concipit auras.
Tempore durescit, mollis fuit herba sub undis.

Millions of pious Swedish people have sat puzzling over words such as these, without understanding the Latin quotation and in blissful ignorance of the fact that Ovid is hardly the most suitable author to be quoted in a book of family sermons, but filled with the conviction that meditation on the shoals of herrings was part of true Christian worship.

When in the next chapter Arndt treats of God's work on the sixth day, his exposition is noticeably reminiscent of an old-fashioned type of nature-study book. He goes through a list of all the animals mentioned in the Bible, exhorting the reader to admire and reflect on their noteworthy qualities, nor does he overlook the edible aspect:

One may now muse upon the myriad and multifarious kinds of creatures which are in the air, on the earth and in the sea; for all of them has God provided not solely for the bare necessities of life and for their pleasure and delight, but has created for each and every kind its special food, according to its species and its character; and all this from His fatherly solicitude.

It is certain that Kolmodin had such words of Arndt in his mind when he wrote his lovely hymn:

> O bless the yearly harvest,
> And water, Lord, our land.

One cannot of course draw up any statistics of the number of Swedish clergy who used these particular extracts from Arndt's *The True Christianity* as their text for edifying discourses. But one can rest assured that they were not few. One must bear in mind, too, that although in those days the clergyman belonged to a different class from the peasant, he usually had a farmer's interests and knowledge. Over and over again pastors and curates were praised, not only because they had preached God's word clearly and simply, but also because they had performed an act pleasing to God by distributing handbooks relating to the preparation of flax or the cultivation of hops or the keeping of bees. The road between theology and economics was quite short. The proper contemplation of the usefulness of animals and plants was an important part of the Christian faith — this one learned from Arndt. In Stenbrohult rectory it was committed to memory.

The profane author most read in Stenbrohult rectory was probably Virgil. In the Fourth Book of the Georgics he devotes a song to honey's ethereal syrup, the celestial gift:

The Gifts of Heav'n my foll'wing Song pursues,
Aerial Honey, and Ambrosial Dews.

And he gives a memorial to the bees:

First, for thy Bees a quiet Station find,
And lodge 'em under Covert of the Wind;
For Winds, when homeward they return, will drive
The loaded Carriers from their Ev'ning Hive.

Wild Thyme and Sav'ry set around their Cell;
Sweet to the Taste, and fragrant to the Smell:
Set rows of Rosemary with flow'ring Stem,
And let the purple Vi'lets drink the Stream.[1]

Nils Linnæus's second son, the Rev. Samuel Linnæus, the good economist, wrote a noteworthy booklet which had for its title: *Short but reliable Bee-Keeping, founded and set up on personal experience and investigations conducted according to the Queen-Bee's proper nature and attributes.*

The book was printed in Växjö in 1768. The Rev. Samuel Linnæus had probably been influenced up to then by what his elder brother had written, though the literary impression may not have been over-strong. Broadly speaking, it was very likely the preaching of Nils Linnæus which Samuel Linnæus carried further when in these words he expounded the gospel according to the bees:

In this respect one may behold with the greatest wonderment God's wise disposition, even with these small creatures. — Who must not marvel at their diligence? At their ingenious work? Why, the greatest artist must admit that he is too unskilled to make a single honeycomb so cunningly, even if he were able to buy the raw materials for it from the bees. — And how may a Christian not rejoice when, during leisure moments in beholding God's work, he perceives the traces of such a wise Creator's gentle hand, which, when it is opened, fills all living things with delight. — A poor countryman often does not know what he is to find as food morning and evening for his children, himself and household, or what he is to get to pay the taxes, to all of which bees could amply contribute.

[1] *The Works of Virgil*, translated into English verse by Mr. Dryden, London, 1721.

It is strange that none of Carl Linnæus's biographers has taken this book by Samuel Linnæus into account. It bears evidence of piety, theoretical fervour and practical utilitarianism. Had the boy who was born at Råshult died as a baby, one could still have spoken of a Linnæan contribution to the history of Swedish culture. The joy of beauty, the fear of God, practical interests, theoretical passion — these were an inheritance in the Stenbrohult rectory, gathered by Nils Linnæus, administered by Samuel Linnæus, transformed by Carl Linnæus into what is our people's greatest historical literary achievement.

*   *   *

> My child, what do I see! Plants in my Bible!
> How dares my Charlie disarray
> The sacred book like that! 'Tis sinful.

Thus might have spoken Mrs. Christina Linnæus in an old cycle of poems *The Flower King*, once diligently read and much admired, but nowadays perhaps unjustly despised and forgotten. And the picture of the boy in Stenbrohult playing with plants has become familiar to all who know the name of Linnæus.

Originally, indeed, it bore the impress of Linnæus himself. In his many more or less discursive autobiographical sketches he has, in wonderment at his strange destiny, lingered over these first poetic childhood memories. He was proud of his origin, pleased at being the first-born of a young husband and wife deeply in love with each other, which in his medical dissertations he considers especially happy, glad to have been born, 'just in the most beautiful spring-time, when the cuckoo proclaimed the summer between *mensis frondescentiæ* and *mensis florescentiæ*', as he puts it in *Handwritten Memoranda*; but above all he liked to dwell in his recollections on his earliest encounters with the world of plants.

It is quite another matter whether Linnæus, especially in remarks made in his old age, did not view his childhood in retrospect not entirely in keeping with reality. Linnæus had a romantic conception of his life's difficulties and conflicts. But quite a short time after his death his younger brother, the recently quoted Samuel Linnæus, noted down in a most remarkable letter what tradition in Stenbrohult rectory then had to say about the childhood days of the great man now dead. This letter must be regarded as the most authentic source of information about the boy Carl Linnæus and part of it may be quoted here:

When in the year 1705 [the Rev. Samuel Linnæus tells us] our late father removed to Råshult, which is the curate's domicile at Stenbrohult, he laid out a little garden there (for he was a great lover of botany, though at that time it was not as it is now). In this he set divers plants, preferably such as had beautiful flowers. His young, newly-married wife, who had not seen their like (scarcely a single garden in fact), delighted in the garden's charm. In this garden father had made with his own hands an elevation like a circular table, round which were beds of herbs and shrubs to represent the guests, and flowers to represent the dishes on the table. Our mother would very often gaze on this and at that period my brother was conceived. Pretty flowers were displayed for her in the late autumn and made her long for the spring, when many more would appear. A pious, good and God-fearing husband endeavoured to make the time pass quickly for her. The 13th May 1707 was a grievous day, for with very great pain and danger to her life she brought forth a well-proportioned son and she had wanted the child to be of the gentler sex. 'Now I have reason for having suffered', said she. But her husband was all the happier, and his joy took away her sorrow, and with gladness they had this, their first child, christened on the 19th of the same month. As soon as the child could take the smallest notice the father, who was inquisitive and dearly loved his little son, began to adorn the cradle with flowers, especially when he came from the garden. The following year the father took his little son out with him, sometimes into the garden and sometimes into the meadow, often laying the child on the ground in the grass and leaving in its hand a flower to play with.

In 1708 our parents removed to Stenbrohult, as father was now rector instead of perpetual curate as before. In 1709 he laid out a garden there: transferring both trees and plants from Råshult — not all, for a number still survive there. The lad began to walk and this was father's greatest delight along with working in the garden. Carl saw his father's labour as of the greatest importance and soon began to wish to garden too. He was given one or two small beds to sow and weed and thus was born his great love for plants and trees. These beds were later changed for an allotment which was called Carl's garden. Then came the time when Carl must begin his studies. He had wits enough, but his mind was mostly on the garden. His mother would scold him for this, but the patient father always took his only son's part.

The year 1716 was a melancholy one, for young Carl had to go to Växjö, but it was even more so in 1717 when he was initiated into school life. The then Rector Scholæ Mag. Daniel Lannærus, a close friend of father's, would often invite little Carl to his home, and also into the garden to play and to eat berries (for the head master was also a great lover of everything appertaining to the knowledge of plants). The Doctor asked little Carl about one or two plants, and whether he knew such and such a plant's name? Carl answered promptly and even asked the Doctor questions. He thus received not merely scholastic instruction, but also had the opportunity of learning the names of many plants. The Doctor's favour, which increased more and more, made little Carl very happy to be in Växjö.

During the holidays at home Carl amused himself with his brother and sisters, knew their least illnesses by their pulse, made himself bleeding irons of wood, as though he were going to bleed them: at times he would go in search of plants with which to cure his sisters. The Doctor speaks of little Carl's love of botany to his friend Rothman, then teacher and Med. Provincialis, who calls Carl to him, takes him into his garden, forms an unbelievable liking for the boy and gives him permission at all times to go into his garden, where there were several kinds of plants. Carl makes the stipulation with Rothman and Doctor Lannærus that they would not speak of his passion to his parents, who could never imagine his being anything other than a theologian; never reflecting that their own actions had laid the foundation in him for botany. Carl went to school and did his lessons merely for the sake of appearances, and to avoid caning and seeing his classmates leave him behind.

One of Carl's greatest difficulties was nerving himself to disclose his *vitae genus* to his parents. To his mother he simply did not dare. At last a propitious occasion arose for him: one or two friends came to Stenbrohult; father takes them out into the garden, they sit round a small table on seats specially made for it and have a talk over their glasses of ale. During the conversation father says: 'Yes, it is always so: where there is a will there is a way.' Carl, who was always there if anyone went into the garden, took these words *ad notam*. When the visitors were gone and his father went to the abovementioned table, Carl goes up to him and asks him if it was true, what dear father said when the visitors were here. Father, who was always joking and in a gay mood, asked what it was he had said. But Carl wants a definite answer. Then Carl repeats father's words. Father replied that it was indeed so: 'provided one's inclination falls on something good', he added. Whereupon Carl says: 'Well, father, never ask me again to be a priest, because for that I have no inclination at all.'

Alas, this was a thunderbolt for father, who had always cherished such a great love for his Carl. He was scarcely able to speak; but at last, astounded and dismayed, asks what he wanted to be in that case? 'Well', says Carl, 'I want to apply myself to medicine and botany.' Father answers: 'You know your parents' impecunious circumstances, and that the study you wish to choose is very costly.' Carl takes father at his word and says: 'If those words are true that my father has said, means will not be lacking for me.' Father answers, with tears in his eyes and in great distress: 'May God give you fortune then, I shall not compel you to anything for which you have no inclination.' Father sees to Carl's books, and they were changed from theology to med. and bot. Father did not dare for nigh on 1 year reveal to his own dear wife that Carl was a medical student, for it would have upset her more than if he had changed his religion. Mother at last learns of this with grief: it almost gave her a stroke. Her only consolation, that she still had a son, Samuel, whom one should protect from the garden.

This artless account has both a singular charm and an authentic ring. One notices that the tension between the boy's inclination on the one hand and the pressure of environment and pedagogic lack of understanding on the other, depicted in such vivid colours in older descriptions of the Stenbrohult legend, is here not very pronounced. When reading Samuel Linnæus's letter one gets the impression that no gardener could have selected soil for a rare plant with greater care, or watched over its growth with more solicitude, than the Fates who spun the thread of this boy's life.

Linnæus himself tells us in his *Handwritten Memoranda:*

Carl was barely four when on one occasion he accompanied his father to a collation at Möcklanäs, in the most beauteous summertime, and when towards evening the guests were resting in a green meadow, the rector expounded to the company how each flower had its name, together with much that was wondrous and remarkable about plants, showing the roots of *Succisa, Tormentilla, Orchides,* and many more. The boy gazed at these with great delight; the talk struck a sympathetic chord in the boy's genius. After this the father had no peace from the boy, who constantly asked the names of plants far more numerous than the father could answer, but often forgot the names as children do, and he was on one occasion sternly spoken to by his father, who said that he would never give him any more names if he forgot them again. After that the boy's whole heart and soul was set on remembering the names, so that he might never lose his greatest pleasure.

Later, in the year 1735, when Linnæus was about to set out for unknown destinies abroad, his old father besought him, according to what is told in *Iter ad Exteros,* to take care of his library in the event of anything happening to him before his son's return home. This would seem to indicate that the book collection at Stenbrohult was not of the meanest. It does not appear, however, to have contained many works on natural science, for in his autobiography Carl Linnæus points out that as a lad he night and day studied 'wretched guides' in botany, old herbal authorities like Arvid Månsson of Rydaholm, Tillands and Palmberg. Great botanists like Bromelius and Rudbeck were as yet out of his reach.

Works such as Arvid Månsson's *Book of Herbs* are interesting to us today from the aspect of cultural development. Even the old plant names are full of poetry, and it is gladdening to read such a description of the plant balm as this:

'It rejoices the heart and drives away melancholy.'

But the author's viewpoint — and this applies to most of the old herbal books — is exclusively practical; he mentions plants according to their usefulness to health, they being of no interest to him in any other connection. Thus in Månsson's book there is much cogitation concerning the importance wormwood (*Artemisia vulgaris*) may have for the female sexual organs, whereas there is no mention of this pleasant grey plant's structure or prevalence. Plants were of interest in so far as they were of benefit to the apothecary or in the kitchen, otherwise not at all.

In his capacity as doctor, Linnæus was later to credit plants with an extraordinarily great medical significance, but this was never of primary importance to him. His aesthetic joy in the world of plants must at a very early stage have fused into his curiosity concerning their names, their nature. And it was the names he asked for first. He was always to assert later on that names were the way to knowledge of a thing. For Linnæus the world was indeed created in the beginning by the word. A statement such as the following from the foreword to the *Journey in Västergötland* applies up to a point even to the boy in Stenbrohult:

If I mention eye, birch, perch, or black cock, and the reader does not understand what is meant by these names, he will make but little headway with the text. Nomina si pereunt, perit et cognitio rerum.

It was for the sake of the names that the boy read the old herbal books in his father's library. But this also contained a guide within the world of nature which could not be called wretched. It is known that Carl Linnæus himself as a student counted among his collection of books a copy of Aristotle's *Historia Animalium*, which had been a present from his father. One may rightly suppose that Nils Linnæus is unlikely to have come across this work in Stenbrohult, but that he had brought it with him from Lund, and that it therefore was among the first books his son had been able to read as soon as he had a good command of Latin. At the end of the book the young Carl Linnæus has, moreover, made a small note of the author's fee of gigantic dimensions which Aristotle received from Alexander for his labours in natural science. It no doubt crossed the student's mind that another naturalist might well likewise win fame and fortune, nor was this anticipation disappointed.

The importance of *Historia Animalium* for Carl Linnæus would be difficult to over-estimate. In this book he found first and foremost what had been missing in the herbal books: a great natural system. Here he learned that nature's forms are the stamp of divine reason on the substance of matter; it is a way of thinking very suggestive of that underlying all Linnæus's own systematic works. Here he read about the animal world from a viewpoint untouched by practical utilitarian claims, the viewpoint of coherence, of the theoretical conception of unity. In short, it was the world of science that revealed itself to the boy in Stenbrohult when for the first time he got down to reading *Historia Animalium*.

In the very first book of Aristotle's work there occurs a statement that probably gave the young student much food for thought. Aristotle begins his long anatomical investigation of animals with these words:

To begin with, we must make an examination of the parts of a man's body. For just as each nation makes economic calculations in the currency to which it is most accustomed, so must we proceed in other matters in a like manner. And of course man is the species of animal with which all of us are the most familiar.

When Linnæus was subsequently to cause annoyance by incorporating man in his table of four-footed animals in *Systema Naturæ*, this way of looking at things was neither new nor revolutionary to him. He had previously made himself conversant with it in his study of Aristotle. Also in his conception of the aim of existence and the essence of piety he was later on to show that he followed in the Greek thinker's footsteps.

In *Historia Animalium* Aristotle has made the first coherent attempt at a uniform animal systematism. After bodily structure, manner of living and habits, the animals are divided up into groups and sub-groups. These sub-divisions fall naturally into place and are conditioned, among other things, by language. A general term like 'bird', presupposes, of course, a primary sub-division of species. But Aristotle combined the animal groups into a system which on the whole endured until the boy in Stenbrohult who read his work produced a new and better one.

But *Historia Animalium* was also without doubt Linnæus's first textbook in concrete detailed knowledge concerning the life of animals. Approximately 520 species are mentioned and partly characterized in Aristotle's work. Even the incorrect particulars made some impression on Linnæus. A number of birds migrate, but a number hibernate, Aristotle says. 'The swallow, for instance, has been found in holes, entirely divested of its feathers.' As far as I can see, this remark is due to confusion with the bat; Linnæus stubbornly maintained that the swallow spends the winter at the bottom of the lake, which is no better. But in his treatise of 1757 on the migration of birds, Linnæus states that the stork too hides itself in the water during the winter; he refers there to an ornithologist in Danzig, but the statement derives in the last resort from *Historia Animalium*. But these curiosities are of secondary importance compared with the fact that Aristotle showed Linnæus a form of animal characterization which he himself was to keep to in his scientific writings and in his lectures. What these two natural scientists' works have in common is an extraordinary concentration, a breath-taking swiftness of delineation, which often contains some special, concrete detail or circumstance peculiar to the species in question, something that in Linnæan terminology can be called curious. As examples, here are one or two descriptions of birds taken quite at random from *Historia Animalium*:

The wren lives in thorny thickets and clefts; it is difficult to catch, keeps out of the way, has a harmless disposition, finds its food easily and is almost a master of building. It has been given the nickname of 'old man' or 'king', and tradition has it that for this reason it lives at enmity with the eagle.

It is at once the anecdotal quality and the sharp, concise statement of essential facts that is so conspicuously like Linnæus. Aristotle writes of the green linnet:

The green linnet, so named because of the colour of the belly, is as big as a lark; it lays four or five eggs, builds its nest with the aid of a plant called comfrey, which it pulls up by the roots, and makes an under-mattress to lie on of hair and wool.

The tree-creeper is characterized even more briefly:

The tree-creeper is an intrepid little bird, it lives among the trees, feeds on caterpillars, which it finds in abundance, and its warble is strong and clear.

It is easy to see that Linnæus, for example in his *Lectures on the Animal Kingdom*, came very close to the Aristotelian pattern. But its significance is even wider than this.

I have [wrote Linnæus later concerning the accounts of his travels], set down things quite briefly, without much argument or many reflections, which always speak for themselves when the data are correct, and all this that I might gain brevity, which is the most pleasant way of writing.

This stylistic ideal he learnt from *Historia Animalium*.

* * *

Although it was by the father's guidance that the child at Stenbrohult, and with the help of Aristotle that the half-grown boy got his first bearings in the world of nature, it is also likely that he often listened to what the peasants of the surrounding countryside had to say about the portents of trees and animals, about sacred trees, herbs, and animals. One must not, however, over-estimate the importance of this primitive nature cult in Linnæus's life's work. It must have happened that the boy in his teens more often smiled to himself and shook his head than nodded agreement when listening to the harmless superstition of farm-hands and maid-servants. He was soon enough to speak hard words of gnomes and sorcery, and as a stern reformer he was to wage unrelenting war on old poetical plant names connected with saintly legends and pious popular belief. But sometimes he no doubt listened attentively when old people interpreted bird-song; when his father now and then wearied of his questions, or was too busy to answer, the boy must have been glad that there were many in the parish with whom he could discuss what was dearest to his heart.

Even when he was to explain the Lappland flora to the learned men of Europe he did not forget, as we shall see later on, to recall the Stenbrohult inhabitants' interest in plants. In his *Journey in Skåne* he speaks of the king-fern, *Osmunda regalis*, of which then, as much later, there was but a single specimen growing wild in the stream at Fanhult. Linnæus tells us:

The wise woman Ingeborg of Mjärhult, when she lived at Mjärhult, used to go to this shrub of a morning, silent and fasting, to take counsel of I know not whom, whence the inhabitants of Virestad called the shrub 'Ingeborg of Mjärhult's pulpit'.

Even when Hyltén-Cavallius was writing about Värend and its inhabitants the lone king-fern, growing in the same place, was used by a wise old man as a powerful remedy. Such things caught the fancy of the young Linnæus not merely because

47

they were picturesque. He was always to believe in the healing power of plants. His services to Sweden's pharmacopoeia were due to an interest, a conviction, which the peasants of Stenbrohult might well have helped to kindle within him.

But if he never believed in the portents of trees and animals, as a child he did listen with pleasure to fairy-tales and legends about hares and foxes, cuckoos and swallows, about black-cocks and doves and wrens, snakes and slow-worms, which in Värend, according to Hyltén-Cavallius, were for ever on people's lips. The belief that the cuckoo was changed into a hawk in the autumn was assiduously opposed by Linnæus in his scientific writings. He soon ceased no doubt to credit that the toad and the frog were sacred, the toad because it was a gnome in disguise, the frog because it was an enchanted princess, but he learned to listen to their croaking with pleasure even though he always regarded amphibians as horrid animals. He is unlikely to have given a girl nine flowers to put under her pillow on Midsummer's Eve, but he perhaps helped the dairymaids to find them. When the churches in Värend were decked with leaves at festival times, and the cottages strewn with wildflowers in summer and with juniper branches in winter, Linnæus rejoiced at the custom, even if he was never in touch with its origin in ancient Nordic folk lore.

When the country children went picking berries, they used first of all to scatter them in the air, exclaiming: 'This is for the black woodpecker.' Linnæus must have known quite early that the black woodpecker lives on insects and not on berries, but on his way home with the children he joined with them in watching out for the bird. Such was the affinity and such was the difference. The peasants of Värend were loth to mention the weasel by name: they feared that it would then cause harm. But Linnæus loved to mention it by name. He dreamt of being able to call every animal and plant by its name. His eye was clearer. His focal point was different.

* * *

The countryside of Stenbrohult, his father's pious faith, inspired by Arndt, in the ability of creation to reveal the

Creator, and the first initiation into Aristotle's zoological system, these were the most important factors in Linnæus's development during his boyhood years. At Växjö College he was a mediocre pupil. But he kept abreast of his classmates and was by no means their inferior. He learned to speak and write Latin and become familiar with Virgil and Ovid. The school regulations gave very little scope for natural history, but Doctor Rothman seems to have been an inspiring teacher. He presented the school-boy with an elementary work in medicine, *Prevotii Medicina Pauperum*. Linnæus could also afford to buy works on natural history which had nothing to do with the school curriculum, though he often complained of the cost. During his last years at school he certainly had a far deeper and more comprehensive knowledge than even a gifted and studious matriculation candidate of today.

In one branch the Växjö school-boy was already well versed. Rothman was by nature a scholar of broad perception whose scientific achievements, owing to unfortunate material circumstances, never equalled his talents. But he took care of his pupil. He initiated him into Tournefort's system, the finest of the age as regards the classification of plants. And it has recently been established by an English scientist, S. Savage, that in 1726 Rothman also introduced the young Linnæus to Vaillant's remarkable theories on the sexuality of plants. It is not unlikely that the young scholar, as he left the handsome, newly built school, in front of which at that time the waves lapped much higher than they do now, and walked along the shore fingering the bulrushes and the sedge, already sensed the first hazy outlines of the new botanical system that was to be associated with his name.

Any lack of attention he may have shown to school work was only of the kind that necessarily accompanied his disposition, his especial genius. The school curriculum at that time included, *inter alia*, Bible-reading in one's mother tongue. What we can safely say of Linnæus at school is that he was thinking more of the picture's factual content than of its allegorical-religious worth as he declaimed Jeremiah's words:

Yea, the stork in the heaven knoweth her appointed times; and the turtle and the crane and the swallow observe the time of their coming; but my people know not the judgment of the Lord.

In this respect, moreover, Linnæus thought the holy scripture was wrong, and that swallows did not migrate. This he had learnt of an even greater authority — Aristotle.

CHAPTER III

THE FLORAL NUPTIALS

HISTORICAL lines of demarcation are risky. The age to which Linnæus belonged has been called the 'Linnean' after him, and there is no doubt about the reason: in eighteenth-century Sweden the interest, both scientific and poetic, shown in natural history is felt to have been due to Linnæus's illustrious work and stimulating influence, and in one way of course this is right. The name of Linnæus unquestionably marks a milestone in our cultural development. But on the other hand it must not be forgotten that the ground was well prepared for reception of his ideas. *Curiositas naturalis* was not an unknown concept at our Swedish seats of learning when Linnæus was an undergraduate. 'Gallant heroes lived before Agamemnon, not a few.' Linnæus was fortunate not only in his environment but in the moment.

The splendid advance gained in natural scientific study in England during the latter half of the seventeenth century was also of great importance to the Swedish world of learning. This applied primarily to the exact natural sciences: mathematics and mechanics. Botany and zoology were not considered by the sorely distressed rulers of the Swedish state to have the same degree of usefulness. Interest in botany had cooled somewhat in Upsala when, during the great fire of 1702, the manuscripts of the elder Rudbeck's gigantically conceived work *Campi Elysii* and thousands of completed wood-cut blocks had been destroyed. Rudbeck the younger never had the means or opportunity of publishing his magnificent bird drawings. But *Curiositas naturalis* existed.

It may be said that the two Rudbecks demonstrated natural science's feeble power of attraction at the time by turning their backs on it in their middle age and applying their research and exuberant imagination to humanism. But specialization was rare in those days, and an equally telling circumstance is that a man like Erik Benzelius the younger, who was a clergyman and humanist, was greatly disturbed in his philological and painstakingly erudite historical investigations by his inability to check his delight in dabbling in natural scientific matters.

It was not everyone who approved of the tendencies of the age as evinced by the activities of Benzelius. To the critical belonged the most original thinker Sweden possessed at the beginning of the eighteenth century, the clear-sighted and warm-hearted Professor Anders Rydelius in Lund. He was an ardent Cartesian, and all adoration of, or even keen interest in, nature was in his eyes an abomination. Repeatedly he uttered trenchant words of warning against *magia naturalis*. In his *Exercises in Reason* he exclaims: 'Aristotle had an everlasting *magia naturalis* in his blood.' The strange thing is, he writes in one of his Latin treatises, 'that people are so diligent and zealous in the investigation of stones and metals, and set great store by this art of research, whereas the knowledge of objects by which not only all things, but also all arts and sciences, are judged is either rejected as simple or disdained as being easily learnt'. Admiration for nature is, he considers, a deception of reason. And from this viewpoint he prefers to his own age — despite all his Lutheran horror of papacy — the era of scholastic philosophy, when 'seldom was anything impious propounded in the science of the spiritual'.

But his words fell on deaf ears. To the Lund of Anders Rydelius came, on August 17th, 1727, the novice Linnæus, who had *magia naturalis* in his blood to an even greater extent than his master Aristotle.

It is unlikely that the exterior of the South-Swedish university town impressed Linnæus very greatly, even though the only other town he had seen was Växjö, and possibly Kristianstad. Lund was a very small town, an agricultural and market-gardening town with but one long street, on either side of which, in the vicinity of the cathedral, lay the large houses, still reminiscent of the might and supremacy of the Church during the Middle Ages. Otherwise it consisted of narrow passages overgrown with grass where swine and geese waddled up and down. In August, when Linnæus arrived, it was no doubt beautiful, filled with the scent of summer flowers, and in the spring it was rich in bird song. Unhappily, the town was also full of manure the whole year round. When Charles XII lived there ten years before Linnæus he had taken strong exception to all the filth, though he was a king who otherwise was anything but fussy about external appearances. Apart from manure, 'dead cats and dogs, together with other carcases' — to use the words of the official records — used to lie about the streets and alleys in abundance. It was a somewhat unappetizing mud that undergraduates and tutors splashed about in during the long winter months.

In his *Journey in Skåne* 1749 Linnæus wrote of Lund that the university 'has been improved so considerably during the one and twenty years since I studied here that I could scarcely recognize it, for which it largely has to thank its great chancellors, the Gyllenborgs.'

Even in the autumn of 1727 there were, it is true, eminently learned professors at Lund, but the organization of the tuition left much to be desired. In those subjects which especially interested Linnæus, no instruction was given at all. But, as he himself relates subsequently in his biographical notes, he received some compensation for this in that he happened to live with the only natural scientist of note then to be found in Lund, namely Kilian Stobæus.

Linnæus's autobiography must not be taken literally, but his account of being billeted with Stobæus and the dour old professor's transition from wrath to interest, when he found the newly fledged undergraduate immersed in nocturnal studies in his library, is no doubt true enough. He describes Stobæus as 'an ailing man, one-eyed, with one foot shrunken, constantly plagued by migraine, hypochondria, and backache; but otherwise possessed of a matchless genius'. Linnæus received no regular tuition from Stobæus, but he did get something more important: personal contact, conversation on an equal footing, a direct introduction into the workshop of science. During all his youth he was favoured by fortune in never being herded together with other students, and in establishing friendly relations with the grey-haired sages at all the seats of learning he visited.

It is of importance to know what books the young Linnæus became familiar with through the university library.

On March 27th, 1728, he borrowed the Zoological Writings of Aldrovandus. In Stenbrohult he had made the acquaintance of Aristotle, but the gigantic animal books, which had been written during the sixteenth and seventeenth centuries, were no doubt too expensive for the vicarage by Lake Möckeln. In the catalogue of the diocesan library in Växjö the only great zoologist of that period represented is the grand and primitive old sixteenth-century scientist, Gesnerus. Rothman may have owned other books, but all points to the fact that Linnæus, when in Lund, had more need of zoological than botanical works. What he learned and how he learned from these folio volumes is not easy to determine. A book such as the *Historia Naturalis* of Johannes Johnstonus he subsequently spoke of in scathing terms, due to its being systematically weak, and rich in philological comments on fabulous monsters; but it has the best and most beautiful pictures of all the pre-Linnean animal books — the engravings of the shot ruffs, for instance, are masterpieces — and the text contains concrete and curious details. Linnæus — most likely in Lund — learned much from these pictures and the descriptive text.

He was later to speak with most respect of Willoughby's *Ornithologiæ Libri Tres*, a handsome book 'cum iconibus elegantissimis et vivarum avium simillimis', with very beautiful pictures and most like living birds, which pictures, however, all prove on closer inspection to be the same engravings which Johnstonus reproduced much better. But Willoughby had a clearer conception of the sub-division of species. He writes of the division of birds, *De divisione avium*, that birds can be divided into land birds and water birds, 'Aves in genere dividi possunt in terrestres et aquaticas. Terrestres sunt, quæ aquas minime frequentant.' The land birds are those which frequent water to a lesser degree. Rightly observed, but a somewhat loose rule; the undergraduate at Lund, when reading Aldrovandus and Willoughby, must have cogitated as to whether one could not readily find a better, a more exact and more concrete basis of classification.

Besides the private library of Stobæus and the university library, Linnæus had access to another means of research while at Lund, which perhaps was more important than those mentioned: the three kingdoms, animal, vegetable, and mineral, of the surrounding countryside.

Through the youthful Linnæus's writings, not published until a later date, we know quite a lot about the young undergraduate's rambles and excursions to different parts of Skåne. He walked or rode to Lomma and Malmö and Fågelsång, and he accompanied Stobæus to Vittskövle, Köpinge, Ramlösa, and Helsingborg. The immediate result of these expeditions was one or two botanical dissertations on a small scale. Arriving at Upsala the following year he had with him a small completed work called *Spolia Botanica*, in which he had collected, in accordance with Tournefort's system, his botanical discoveries in Småland, Skåne, and Roslågen. The attractive foreword reveals much of what he thought of Småland and Skane:

Smolandiam I deal with first, being my dearly loved native countryside, which is extensively covered with sandy gravel, hills, marshes, heather, pine, spruce, juniper, and prodigious forests. In between, fresh lakes are everywhere to be found, the bottoms of which are of divers kinds, but especially stone, sand, and gravel. Here the seed is commonly sown in the spring, without the earth's being left to lie fallow.

Stenbrohult is a parish which, situated 5 miles from Växjö, down towards the border of Skåne in the hundred of Allbo, seems by comparison with all other places to be like a queen among her sisters; she is also favoured with rare and singular plants, which are seldom or never to be seen elsewhere in the land. Why, the vicarage here seems to have been adorned as it were by Flora herself. Here I have imbibed with my mother's milk the divers forms of the various plants; I greatly doubt if any place in all the world can have a more pleasant situation. Is it thus to be wondered at, if I, with the poet, had cause to complain:

> *Nescio qua natale solum dulcedine cunctos*
> *ducit et immemores non sinit esse sui.*

I will therefore first enumerate a list of the rare plants which are to be found here.

Scania, on the other hand, is quite contrary in soil and situation. Here there are but seldom any forests, heather or lakes; but the whole countryside is a plain consisting of clayey soil and is, rather, a field, as the earth is commonly ploughed up and sown every three years, and quite different plants are found here from those in Småland, though corresponding quite well with those that grow in Upland.

Lund, containing the University, which I attended for but one year, has in its environs most of the plants that will be enumerated here, which I came to examine all the more carefully as in 1728 I had several students there to initiate in botany. The marine plants I have taken either at Malmö or Lomma 6 miles from Lund, where I would go now and again to collect fossils in the sand by the sea-shore. Fågelsång is an estate three-quarters of a mile from Lund, where nature has made her theatres and works of art. Here there is a high slope of pyrites, cloven as it were into two parts, through which runs a stream. On either side facing the brook it is overgrown with thickets, in which are to be found all kinds of the rarest plants. Here one might well avow that the gods have had their seat for, of all places in the world, this is the pleasantest.

Although this was written at Upsala it is our most important document concerning Linnæus's sojourn in Lund. The twenty-two-year-old author has already shown himself to be a stylist. The reference to Ovid is to be repeated many times, and we shall return to this. But observe how immediately and tenderly the scholar outlines his memory of Stenbrohult; his style of authorship, the voice of his genius, his characteristic phrases, all matured, long before there can be any talk of literary-historical influences. And how gently he has drawn the contours of the Skåne landscape, independently and far ahead of anyone else! This was written in the 1720s, before our Swedish 'Era of Liberty' had outgrown its swaddling-clothes, and when nearly everything else printed and written was encased in stiff Caroline formality. The young eagle had already stretched its wings.

In another of the young Linnæus's writings, to which we shall shortly revert, *Methodus Avium*, can be found other authentic reminiscences of his time in Lund. Its ornithological allusions have a peculiar charm. They speak of what had altered and what still existed in the bird world of Skåne. Of the stork it is said: 'in Scania copiose aliis rarissime'; abundant in Skåne, but elsewhere extremely rare. It is long since there were storks in abundance in Skåne. But what Linnæus notes about the wild swan fortunately still applies: 'Malmogiæ in Scania frequens'; it is common in Malmö in Skåne. It is clear that Linnæus on winter days by the bay of Lomma cast a reflective and admiring glance up at the long white skeins of wild swans. He speaks of them also with special interest in the *Journey in Skåne* 1749. Of the rook he says in *Methodus Avium*: 'In Scania copiose; the cawing of the black flocks across the plains was evidently just as prevalent when Linnæus was a student in Lund as it is now.

The main features of the landscape, the coastal meadows with their bird life and the blue waters of Öresund, all this Linnæus saw as we see it. But otherwise the Skåne in which he rambled about during the autumn term of 1727 and the spring term of 1728 was rather different from the province we now know. It was greener, damper, and more leafy. Also no doubt it gave worse crops, was poorer and dirtier. But the student Linnæus had no time to notice much of social anomalies. He heard the music of the swans in the bay of Lomma.

Later on he was to acquire a more comprehensive view of life, but the whirring of the great wings he would never forget.

*   *   *

In the hope of finding a better ordered academic tuition Linnæus left the Caroline university for ever at the close of the spring term 1728. But it may have been his diligent roaming about on the plains of Skåne that inspired Kilian Stobæus in 1729 to send out other pupils on tours of exploration into the surrounding countryside; in the excerpts from the foreword to *Spolia Botanica* already quoted one notices how the young Linnæus even then speaks of disciples following in his footsteps; in his *Handwritten Memoranda* one or two names are given. Stobæus's instruction for students is somewhat lengthy: but it is not unlike the plan according to which Linnæus later regulated his youthful travels. Unfortunately the records written by Stobæus's pupils concerning their excursions have been lost. It is quite likely that they showed how a Smålander who had only been at Lund for two terms had managed to procure academic standing for something so empiric as botany.

*   *   *

So the pictures in the peep-show change, and from the autumn of 1729 we have another image, so finely chiselled that it seems almost legendary, in the epos that Linnæus — mingling *Dichtung und Wahrheit* — later wrote of his life. The scene is Rudbeck's garden in Upsala, the present Linneanum.

In the autumn of 1729 Linnæus is sitting in the dilapidated Academic Garden describing one or two flowers, when a venerable clergyman enters and asks Linnæus what he was describing, if he knew the plants, if he had studied botany, whence he had come and how long he had been there.

The venerable clergyman was Dr. Celsius the elder, and this encounter had important consequences for the student. After a period of uncertainty and disquietude he was once more taken care of; Olof Celsius took the young man under his wing. The situation in Lund was repeated in Upsala.

The professors, according to our present-day viewpoint, did not give the natural science pupils proper instruction, but with signal intuition and open-mindedness they sought to further the genius whom they met with wonder on the way.

The younger Rudbeck, already grey-haired, was a versatile, superbly all-embracing man of genius like his famous father. After the set-back he had suffered when both his father's and his own magnificently planned botanical and zoological works were destroyed, not only in the fire at Upsala but also on the political funeral pyre of Swedish megalomania, he was forced to devote himself to philological research, the results of which could be published without printing costs burdensome to the State. He continued to lecture on birds, however, exhibiting beautiful pictures which he and several of his pupils had made during a zoological expedition to Lappland.

Linnæus admired these pictures tremendously, and well he might. The copy preserved in the university library at Upsala of Rudbeck's bird pictures, all done or reproduced by Rudbeck himself, made a remarkable impression upon Linnæus coming, as he did, direct from his studies of Gesnerus and Aldrovandus. All are not equally good, and quite a number have faded with the passage of time. Rudbeck's pictures at their best are as living as Audubon's; for instance the horned owl. The smaller owls are poor, the wryneck very bad, the jay faded. But the falcons, all the woodpeckers, the red-backed shrike, the wood pigeon, the yellow-hammer, the chaffinch, the whinchat and the chimney-swallow are brilliant, scarcely surpassed by the Wright brothers.

What this meant to Linnæus should not be under-estimated. In Växjö he had, one may suppose, pondered over the clumsy woodcuts of Gesnerus. In the hard and erroneously drawn lines he had sought to find method and coherence — what a difference between his visual impressions from Stenbrohult and these coarse representations! But when Professor Rudbeck held up his bird pictures during his lectures, the student Linnæus was fired with all the requisite scientific enthusiasm: he recognized their beauty, and that demonstration too could and should be art. Thereafter he was never able to speak of birds without mentioning their gleaming plumage.

*   *   *

The Peter Artedi who was a fellow student of Linnæus at Upsala was almost his equal in scientific talents. He was fated, after many cares and privations, to disappear one night into a black canal in Holland, leaving behind him, among other things, a work on fish which is considered to be epoch-making. From what Linnæus himself has written on the subject it would appear that he felt a warm gratitude and a strong devotion towards Artedi; he was discerning and patient, logical and clear-headed, but he was not born with a caul. When they studied side by side Linnæus gladly let Artedi perfect his knowledge of fish without thought of rivalry; he himself did not care for the cold and slippery creatures. In this friendly competition he was content to go on seeking by himself for a system within a fairer genus, that of the singing, beauteously coloured birds. Even this apportionment of study gives a good indication of the difference between them. Artedi, a scientist pure and simple, probably thought that Linnæus's choice bore witness of frivolity; but with Linnæus it is often hard to differentiate between the theoretical and the aesthetic. Sometimes, as we shall see later on, a third outlook is apparent in Linnæus's writings — the religious. Perhaps Artedi, more clearly than Linnæus, bears the emblem under which science has won and will win its greatest victories. But the fact that the science of Linnæus set its stamp on cultural life, that the 1700s can with justification be called the Linnean century, that with Linnæus the tree of knowledge became one with the tree of life, was because he devoted to his research not merely his reason but all his senses as well.

With the help of Rudbeck's pictures and lectures, the support of the mighty Latin bird books by Gesnerus, Aldrovandus, Johnstonus, Bellonius, and Willoughby, with vivid memories of hours and days in gardens and pastures rich in bird-life, he now compiled for his own use a classification of birds, *Methodus Avium Sviticarum*. It is, admittedly, easy to see that many of the authors made use of by Linnæus possessed greater literary and practical ornithological knowledge than he did; but when one begins reading Linnæus's *Methodus Avium* after dipping into these huge, imposing volumes, it is as if one suddenly came upon a meadow near home after straying in a forest, weary from trying to find a path among the massive boulders. Such is the dilettante's impression, but for that very reason it is perhaps of importance; for here in Linnæus's *Methodus Avium* we encounter for the first time the method of distinguishing between avian genera and species which has now become second nature to us. This method, of course, does not accord entirely with that to be found in the latest editions of the school text-books, but the basis is the same. The layman gets lost with Linnæus's predecessors. He can find his way in *Methodus Avium*.

This is not a negligible point. It was chiefly by observing beak and claw that Linnæus made his classification of species. One wonders if there were not also a purely aesthetic feeling behind this concept, a sense of form in keeping with that of the painter and the sculptor. The method is intuitive. Linnæus had forged ahead very quickly; he was young and had many irons in the fire. But set children to sort colours and it will be seen that neatness and reflection lead to less certain results than the possession of a sensitive eye. It has been pointed out that this improvised doctrine is in certain cases superior to the systematism Linnæus perfected towards the end of his life, in which new experiences were carefully weighed in the scales of deliberation. In *Methodus Avium* he has seen — seen quite sensuously with his bright eyes, seen the birds as Leonardo da Vinci saw the human muscles — that birds of prey, parrots, owls, all the crow family, waders large and small, the various kinds of duck, long-winged web-footed birds, struthious birds, poultry, climbing birds, sparrows, etc., all belonged together in their own way, forming a pattern, a living fabric whose warp and woof could best be determined by observing beak and claw. Behind the empiric method is an aesthetic conception.

*   *   *

One can form some idea of the younger Rudbeck's way of lecturing thanks very largely to a number of fragmentary notes made by his listeners. The following note, which can almost certainly be attributed to P. Artedi, dates from the academic year 1727-28. The Martin referred to in the text was an associate professor, Rudbeck's son-in-law and for several years his deputy, when he himself gave up natural history for the labours of philological research.

Since my son-in-law, the late Doctor Martin, has lectured not only several times about botany but also this last term about *regno minerali*, and likewise through a *collegium chemicum* has treated of these matters more fully, but now through his unforeseen decease has occasioned me to complete these works, who otherwise by the King's gracious dispensation am exempted therefrom by reason of my *Lexicon harmonicum linguarum Europæ et Asiæ*, on which I am still working, I have now undertaken to read *de regno animali* to my honoured listeners, beginning *de avibus*.

Whereupon I find, concerning the method, that Gesnerus, who has followed the alphabet, has little or no system. Aldrovandus, on the other hand, begins with the largest birds, the eagle, the kite, the long-eared owl and so on, but as *natura non facit saltum*, I humbly maintain that it is better to begin with the delicate and smaller ones and so work up to the others. However, let us discuss the classification of the birds more fully later on, when we have carefully examined the drawings which I shall have the honour to show my esteemed listeners, in an extensive and costly work upon which I have laboured for several years and which I have had painted to the life both as to colour and size. Yet we also find in the Holy Scripture that the birds have been classified; for in Gen. I. is mentioned *ops calaps*, which is the same as *avis calata* and may mean the water birds, those we call *palmipedes* or swimming birds, which the Jews were forbidden to eat because of their train-oil taste, just as noxious and unclean animals were forbidden because of leprosy.

Later on, in another passage, *ops seeretz* is mentioned, which can be interpreted as *aves terrestres et fissipides*, although they seek their food by the shore. Again, there is mention in the Holy Scripture of *ops scanaim*, the birds of the sky, which no doubt means *aves altevolantes et rapaces, qui cadaveribus victitant*, all of which were forbidden with the Jews, nor do any of our own people willingly eat them. More particularly in Lev. XI, v. 13 there are to be found the following words:

And these are they which ye shall have in abomination among the fowls; they shall not be eaten, they are an abomination: the eagle, and the ossifrage, and the ospray, And the vulture, and the kite after his kind; Every raven after his kind; And the owl, and the night hawk, and the cuckow, and the hawk after his kind, And the little owl, and the cormorant, and the great owl, And the swan, and the pelican, and the gier eagle And the stork, the heron after her kind, and the lapwing, and the bat, All fowls that creep, going upon all four, shall be an abomination unto you.

Whereby divers matters are called to mind, but it is not our intention to dwell upon them here.

Having got thus far in his discourse Professor Rudbeck apparently produced his coloured bird drawings, passing from sounds to things, demonstrating wrens and redstarts. The undoubtedly enthralled audience must nevertheless have found it difficult to grasp the connection between the biblical-philological preamble and the practical object-lesson. Which was the essential and which the non-essential? A learned, aspiring student of an inquiring mind such as the subsequent bishop Göran Wallin told himself instantly that the illustrations must be sheer frivolity; correct and fertile natural research must consist of continuous religious and bibliographical commentaries on various animal and plant names. But there must have been one or two students who began to suspect that the philological discussion was something quite apart which had very little to do with concrete natural science. If the recorder of the lectures really was Artedi he certainly would have made this reflection, resolving thereafter to isolate concrete observation of nature from theological and philosophical speculations. Through this decision the snake of the age changed its skin.

*   *   *

The aesthetic element in the young Linnæus's first draft of a coherent natural system is most apparent in the wonderful dissertation in which for the first time he specified his conception of the sexuality of plants. It was not a question of entirely new discoveries: proof of plants' sexuality had been put forward by Camerarius and Vaillant. Linnæus wanted to replace the hitherto loose philology by exact natural science, but he does it in language that here and there is pure poetry, the clearest and purest that was written in Sweden during the 1720s.

This is how he begins:

In the springtime, when the bright sun comes to our zenith it awakens in all bodies the life that has lain smothered during the cold winter. And then all creatures which in the winter have been dull and sluggish grow more spirited and active; behold, all the birds begin to sing and twitter which have been silent all the winter; behold, all the insects come forth from their hiding-places, in which they have lain half dead during the winter; behold, all the plants spring up and all the trees burst into leaf which in the winter lay dormant, why, man himself seems to acquire new life. For as Pliny said, not without wisdom:

Sole nihil utilius.

This sun affords such joy to all living things that words cannot express it; the black-cock and the wood-grouse can be seen to mate, the fish to play, why, all animals feel the sexual urge. Love even seizes the very plants, as among them both *mares* and *feminæ*, even the hermaphrodites, hold their nuptials, which is what I now intend to discuss, and show from the genitalia of the plants themselves which are *mares*, which *feminæ* and which hermaphrodites.

Such are the introductory words to Linnæus's scientific writings. Neither before nor after him have academic dissertations been written in such a style. The most remarkable thing is that this literary style is so completely unhampered by the fashion of the age. It is neither baroque nor rococo. Its simple freshness reminds one most of the thirteenth-century English folk song, 'Sumer is icumen in, Lhude sing cuccu!' It is quite spontaneous, the most readily occurring expression for something seen and felt. Independent of all so-called trends poets of every age have sung in this strain. There is the same melody in the *Carmina burana*, the medieval spring songs of the wandering scholars:

> *Fronde nemus induitur,*
> *jam canit philomena,*
> *cum variis coloribus*
> *jam prata sunt amœna.*
> *Spatiare dulce est*
> *per loca nemorosa;*
> *dulcere est carpere*
> *jam lilium cum rosa;*
> *dulcissimum est ludere*
> *cum virgine formosa.*

Having respect for the nature of the subject, Linnæus's language is more typical of the age when he reveals the intimate union during the floral nuptials. It is the Caroline epithalamium which re-echoes in this botanical description:

The actual petals of the flower (*petala*) contribute nothing to generation, serving only as Bridal Beds, which the great Creator has so gloriously arranged, adorned with such noble Bed Curtains and perfumed with so many sweet scents, that the Bridegroom there may celebrate his *Nuptias* with his bride with all the greater solemnity. When the bed is thus prepared, it is time for the Bridegroom to embrace his beloved Bride and surrender his gifts to her: I mean, one can see how *testiculi* open and emit *pulverem genitalem*, which falls upon *tubam* and fertilizes *ovarium*.

Neither here nor elsewhere in his treatise on the floral nuptials does Linnæus boggle at using animal designations for the plants' fructification organs. But the description is not clumsy, nor is it dry and medical. The task which professional writers have often set themselves, namely, to describe the sexual act in beautiful, resounding words — and in most cases have utterly failed in, managing only to produce instead of poetry something akin to pornography — is here admirably accomplished by Linnæus. In his presentment a floral radiance is even shed upon the vital animal functions. This can only be attained by a writer who is a poet by nature.

But Linnæus was also, and to a much greater extent, a born scientist. In one respect, however, his discourse is less miraculous than one might suppose. As already mentioned, Linnæus was familiar (much earlier than he was subsequently willing to admit) with Vaillant's theories concerning the sexuality of plants. When the English botanist Savage, at an annual meeting of the Linnean Society in London, announced that he had found notes concerning the botanical studies of Linnæus during the autumn and spring terms 1726-27, which *inter alia* showed that Rothman had initiated him into Vaillant's system, a Swedish scientist who was present, the secretary of the Linné Society, Dr. Arvid Uggla, according to the Proceedings of the Linnæan Society declared that he

wished to emphasize the interesting point about Savage's statement that while still at school Linnæus, through Rothman's teaching, had become aware of Vaillant's ideas about the sexuality of plants as a systematic basis of classification. It was formerly thought (and the belief was supported by Linnæus's own words) that it was not until 1729 that he became acquainted with these theories through a German periodical. But it must be remembered that the information in Linnæus's autobiography is not always reliable, since in later years he was more and more inclined to point out the contrast between his youthful achievements and the difficulties with which he had had to contend. The story of his sexual system's development is clearer now we know that the idea had lain germinating in his mind for many years.

In his thesis on the floral nuptials Linnæus himself touches on Vaillant. He deplores the French scientist's premature death, mentioning that the latter 'had intended to base his entire botanical method' on his experiments concerning the sexuality of plants; of the results of the investigations which Vaillant had already managed to propound Linnæus adds, however, that he has 'not yet seen' them. This statement Linnæus, had he been pressed, might have been able to justify by saying that he only knew Vaillant's paper in question from Rothman's version and not in the original; but it would have been a sophistic defence, and one must accept the fact that Linnæus would never have admitted his debt to a predecessor. Such was his disposition and we must bear with him.

In his *Handwritten Memoranda* Linnæus subsequently wrote of this work:

Linnæus read in *Actis Lipsiensibus* a notice of Vaillant's tract, *De sexu plantarum*, which particularly pleased him, for he himself had begun to recognize the true significance of *Stamina* and *Pistilla*. Artedi was giving up botany generally but reserved to himself the study of *Plantus Umbellatas* as he wished to perfect his ideas on the sexual system of the group. This turned Linnæus's thoughts to doing the same for the rest of the plant kingdom since he had come to the conclusion that *Stamina* and *Pistilla* were no less distinctive than *Petala* and that they were really the essential parts of the flower. Towards the close of the year the then librarian, Georg Wallin, appeared with a philological thesis, *de Nuptiis Arborum*, and as Linnæus had no opportunity of acting as opposer, he wrote several sheets on the correct relationship of *Sexu Plantarum*, in a botanical manner, and gave the manuscript to Doctor Celsius; it eventually came into the hands of Professor Olof Rudbeck and pleased him so much that he desired to know the young man who had written it.

This is not what happened. Linnæus did not work quite so spontaneously as that. His sexual system was not so improvised. It was, as Uggla said, something which had lain germinating in his mind since his Växjö days.

For the Swedish public, at all events, the contents of the treatise on the floral nuptials were a complete novelty. Copies circulated among the students, and it was these that opened the eyes of Olof Rudbeck the younger to the real qualities of this protégé of Professor Celsius. He then took the unusual step of making the ungraduated young student lecturer in botany. He also appointed him as tutor to his young sons; it was, in fact, in the Rudbeck home that Linnæus pondered over the bird drawings which helped him to compose *Methodus*

Avium. He was soon to have the chance of evincing his gratitude to Rudbeck in a way that both Professor Rudbeck and his son Johan Olof must surely have appreciated.

*   *   *

Another thesis from Linnæus's student years which says quite a lot about the author's mood and way of working is the dissertation on King Charles's Sceptre, *De Sceptro Carolino*. It was publicly discussed in Upsala on June 19th, 1731, with pomp and circumstance and great junketing, as both parties bore well-known names, for young Johan Olof Rudbeck — at this time only twenty — was to defend the thesis under the presidency of Professor Roberg. On the original manuscript the young Master Rudbeck's preceptor Carl Linnæus has noted: 'This thesis I have written in one day for thirty dalers in copper. For this another has received the credit.'

It may have been a hurried piece of work, but it was not slapdash. Linnæus had completed his task with much elegance. Not only inasmuch as his description of *Sceptrum carolinum* is extraordinarily concise and detailed, but also, in the purely literary passages, he has succeeded admirably in striking the Rudbeck tone. For it was in *Lapponia Illustrata* that Olof Rudbeck the younger had given the plant its name, and Linnæus now makes Johan Olof Rudbeck write:

When my father, as was said, discovered it, he did not hesitate for long to call so fine and stately a plant after the great king Charles XII, for no plant could so well serve at the same time to construe so great a king's valour, together with a *sceptrum tanto Heroi digno* (a sceptre worthy of so great a hero), as that which is everywhere surrounded by the crimson bloodstained snouts of stalwart lions, which this plant's flowers so prettily and artfully express that art cannot possibly imitate what nature has simulated here; wherefore too my father in his dedication to *Lapponia illustrata* sings:

... whose flower like a golden helmet gleams
with pale and bloody mouth, and blood-bespattered leaves.

That Linnæus admired these two lines is apparent from the fact that he returns to this quotation in two other parts of the

PEDICULARIS SCEPTRUM CAROLINUM L. (half life size).
KING CHARLES'S SCEPTRE

'... whose flower like a golden helmet gleams
with pale and bloody mouth, and blood-bespattered leaves.'

thesis. But he would scarcely be capable of writing them himself. They express a mood that is entirely foreign to him. He therefore continues to speak, not only in Rudbeck's name, but in Rudbeck's spirit, when a little later on he says:

Should, therefore, any name in the world be worthy of being immortalized in *Botanicis*, even among Kings' names, the honoured memory of this valiant king and hero should surely here be placed before all others.

When reading this one has a feeling that one has reached the decisive borderline between two epochs in the history of our land and people. When Linnæus here pays homage to martial memories and gory deeds of prowess, he is speaking with Rudbeck's voice. But only a little further on in the text he informs us that 'in *methodo Linneana*' the plant should be classified as genus *Didynamia*, species *Tetrandria*.

It is important to point out, therefore, that as early as 1731, at the age of twenty-four, Linnæus had the outlines of a plant system completed. Just how far he had conceived this in detail at this juncture it is difficult to say; it is apparent from the determination indicated above that it does not tally with what he was to put forward some years later in *Systema Naturæ*. But Linnæus was evidently clear in his mind at this stage about the general fundamental principles of his sexual system. Hence the conscious tone that betrays itself when in this treatise he places 'the Linnean method' beside that of the great botanists, Tournefort and Boerhaave. He had saluted the Rudbeck tradition, but as something bygone, something that belonged to the past. His was the future, and he knew it.

In the closing words of the work the Caroline achievements, too, are forgotten. 'O mighty God, Lord and Father of Nature, let *Sceptrum Svecicum* never pass away, but year by year ever flourish and increase, that the inhabitants of Svea, to the end of Nature, may have of her enjoyment, peace, delight, and protection.'

These four desirable things bear the stamp, not of the Rudbeck spirit, but of the Linnean Age.

CHAPTER IV

THE MOUNTAINS OF LAPPLAND

AT 11 o'clock in the forenoon on Friday, May 12th, 1732, Carl Linnæus, 'within half a day of twenty-five years of age', rode northwards from the city of Upsala. The young man was short of stature but sturdily built, and his bright, brown eyes twinkled in a sunburnt face. His clothes consisted of

a light coat of linsey-woolsey cloth without folds, lined with red shalloon, having small cuffs and collar of shag; leather breeches; a round wig; a green leather cap, and a pair of half-boots. I carried a small leather bag, half an ell in length, but somewhat less in breadth, furnished on one side with hooks and eyes, so that it could be opened and shut at pleasure. This bag contained one shirt; two pair of false sleeves; two half shirts; an inkstand, pencase, microscope, and spying-glass; a gauze cap to protect me occasionally from the gnats; a comb; my journal, and a parcel of paper stitched together for drying plants, both in folio; my manuscript Ornithology, *Flora Uplandica*, and *Characteres Generici*. I wore a hanger at my side, and carried a small fowling-piece, as well as an octangular stick, graduated for the purpose of measuring. My pocket-book contained a passport from the Governor of Upsala, and a recommendation from the Royal Academy of Sciences.[1]

During his first halt Linnæus wrote in his diary:

At this season Nature wore her most cheerful and delightful aspect, and Flora celebrated her nuptials with Phoebus.

> *Omnia vere vigent et veris tempore florent*
> *et totus fervet Veneris dulcedine mundus.*

Spring clothes the fields and decks the flowery grove,
And all creation glows with life and love.

[1] *A Tour in Lapland, now first published from the Original Manuscript Journal of the celebrated Linnæus* by JAMES EDWARD SMITH, London, 1811.

Now the winter corn was half a foot in height, and the barley had just shot out its blade. The birch, the alder, and the aspen-tree began to put forth their leaves . . . The lark was my companion all the way, flying before me quivering in the air.

> *Ecce suum tirile, tirile, suum tirile tractat.*

The weather was warm and serene. Now and then a refreshing breeze sprang up from the west, and a rising cloud was observable in that quarter.

Thus Linnæus reached the post-house at Högsta.

Here the forests began to thicken. The charming lark, which had till now attended my steps, here left me; but another bird welcomed my approach to the forest, the throstle, *Turdus minor*, whose amorous warblings from the tops of the Spruce Fir were no less delightful. Its lofty and varied notes rival those of the Nightingale herself.

The often quoted and highly praised words have become justly famous. Nature's and the spirit's springtime, the pale daylight of May across the fields of Uppland, these things have never been described more simply, more spontaneously.

It was at the request of the Society of Science in Upsala that Linnæus began his ride to the North, in order to 'investigate all the three kingdoms of Nature' in Lappland and moreover to study 'the strange manner of living of the inhabitants and the benefits and inconveniences to health consequent thereon'. It was a comprehensive task and a hazardous journey.

The general outline of the tour Linnæus has described clearly and concisely in the preface to *Flora Lapponica*, which was published in Amsterdam in 1737; the résumé is worth quoting. He mentions first that he left Upsala during the spring days of tender green and blossom:

I then continued my journey at a moderate pace through Gävle and Gästrikland, Hudiksvall and Hälsingland, Sundsvall and Medelpad, where I climbed the mountain of Norbyknölen. Soon afterwards I sighted Ångermanland and

Härnösand and penetrated at peril of my life into a cave near the top of a mountain called Skuluberget. The winter, which still beset the upper part of Ångermanland, then prompted less haste with the journey; at length, however, I arrived at Umeå in the province of Västerbotten.

Here I left the main highway and proceeded into the virgin tracts of forest extending to the west, finally gaining the border of Lappland. This I crossed, came to Lycksele and then resigned myself, alone, to the Lapps, whose barbaric customs and speech might almost awaken dread. I pursued my course up the river towards the mountains, gave myself up to the Juktan river, against which I then struggled for a long time, labouring thereafter to penetrate the forests and wade across the marshes that were filled with ice, snow, and cold water, but

> . . . fate forbids; the Stygian floods oppose,
> And, with nine circling streams, the captive soul inclose.

My forces being utterly spent, I had finally to retrace my steps to Västerbotten, shortly visiting new and old Piteå and proceeding through new and old Luleå. Here I again left the highroad and steered my course towards Lappland on the river Lule. Jokkmokk and Kvikkjokk churches were passed, and then my wanderings led me through desolate forests, across hills and sandy heaths. Finally at Mount Vallivari I ascended the Lappland Alps, steered my course westwards with a curve towards the more southern Piteå Lappmark, crossed the highest peaks (the so-called mountain-back), descended from there into the most northerly part of Norway, Finnmarken, wandered around on the shores of the Arctic Ocean, and visited Rörstad and Sallerön.

> . . . . To Avernus it is easy to descend,
> But hard the path if one shall upward wend
> Back to the realm of light.

Though my forces were spent, I once more struggled up on to the fells, whence my course was steered towards Torneå Lappmark. Thereafter I again perceived the regions lying more to the east and left them at last, having had more than enough of hunger, thirst, sweat, roaming about, cold, rain, snow, ice, rocks, mountains, and the language of the Lapps.

It is likely that Linnæus, as soon as occasion offered during his halts, at any hour or place, jotted down his observations of the moment or of the preceding few hours. The book should not be judged as a coherent, carefully prepared account. Its charm, its lyrical beauty, its drastic freshness — everything that makes it so alive — are bound up with the fact that it is throughout a child of the moment, that it is so improvised.

It is idle to try to read into it a fixed and well-founded opinion concerning everything that the traveller met, great and small. What Linnæus thought of the Lapps and of Lappland's swamps and mountains, for instance, depended on the weather from day to day, on whether it was sunny or raining, on whether the air was mild or the wind cut through to the marrow; it depended on whether he himself was as fresh as the morning or felt tired with evening's approach, whether he felt the blood coursing briskly through his veins or whether his stomach was out of order; it depended on the state of the roads, on the condition of his horse, on the thrush's song and the diver's call; it depended on whether his hose were clean or not; in short, his reactions were spontaneous. And that is also why he changed his mind both abruptly and often.

Take for instance his notes for June 2nd, when he is on his way up to Sorsele. It is a bright morning, and the Lapps seem to him enviable. They live, he thinks, in accordance with Ovid's description of the silver age. 'Their soil is not wounded by the plough, nor is the iron din of arms to be heard; neither have the people found their way to the bowels of the earth, nor do they engage in wars to define its boundaries. They perpetually change their abode, live in tents, and follow a pastoral life, just like the patriarchs of old.'

But then both road and weather deteriorated. A driving rain set in. Linnæus sank down into the mire and his boots filled with icy water. With his usual, half joking exaggeration he says that 'had our sufferings been inflicted as a punishment, they would, even in that case, have been cruel; what then had we to complain of?' He had now had enough of the journey. The entire country of the Lapps seemed to him to consist of

73

bogs; he therefore called it Styx. 'A divine could never describe a place of future punishment more horrible than this country, nor could the Styx of the poets exceed it.' He finishes by commiserating with the Lapps: 'The Lapps themselves, born to labour as the birds to fly, could not help complaining, and declared they had never been reduced to such extremity before. I could not help pitying them.'

Is it inconsequential, this? No, every traveller and living person must be inconsistent in the same way. Sven Hedin had varying thoughts, according to circumstances, about the Tibetans and the Tibetan plateau. He has praised Takla-makan's desert and he has cursed it. Linnæus loved the wilds when they smiled at him. When he was tired, soaked to the skin and hungry they lost their charm. It all seems quite natural. On the morning of June 2nd the Lapps were happy in Linnæus's eyes. In the evening they were unhappy. It was because he himself in the morning had been happy in their company, but when evening came he was out of temper.

It must also be remembered that Linnæus had a strong and nimble imagination. It has been pointed out that the sodden track here depicted by Linnæus with a much greater con-scription of superlatives than used by Stanley when describing his penetration of the Congo was in reality only about six miles long. Having got so far he was thoroughly tired of the terrain and did not bother to find any better or drier way into Lapp territory, but retraced his steps without further ado.

He no doubt felt that this day's march was not in actual fact a particularly illustrious exploit, and for that very reason his imagination embellishes in the most glaring colours the discomforts he had endured. The following day, June 3rd, he tells of his meeting with the old Lapp woman; the description is with all justice considered classic:

Her stature was very diminutive. Her face of the darkest brown from the effects of smoke. Her eyes dark and sparkling. Her eyebrows black. Her pitchy-coloured hair hung loose about her head, and on it she wore a flat red cap. She had a grey petticoat; and from her neck, which resembled the skin of a frog, were suspended a pair of large loose breasts of the same brown complexion, but encompassed, by way of ornament, with brass rings.

But this brilliant portrait is surely designed to throw into relief what follows. Linnæus causes this wild apparition to be appalled at his reckless undertaking:

Though a fury in appearance, she addressed me with mingled pity and reserve, in the following terms: 'O, thou poor man! What hard destiny can have brought thee hither, to a place never visited by any one before? This is the first time I ever beheld a stranger. Thou miserable creature! how didst thou come, and whither wilt thou go? Dost thou not perceive what houses and habitations we have and with how much difficulty we go to church?'

The old woman goes on in the same style to protest that no one can proceed any further; in the present state of the roads it is at least seven days' journey to Sorsele. It is of course splendidly told, but it does bear the stamp of fiction. The old Lapp woman, who had never seen any other tract, could hardly have been so appalled at the dreadful isolation of her native countryside. *A Tour in Lappland* is a book to be read with a grain of salt. The writer of this diary was exact as a natural scientist, but where other things were concerned he was apt to magnify or belittle as the mood took him.

This should not give rise to criticism. It is because Linnæus in his diary yields so completely to his moods that it is so full of atmosphere. Take a detail such as this at the beginning of his journey. He is in Gästrikland on May 15th. Linnæus notes that the redstart and the brambling were singing in the wood, and the black-cock could be heard, but the woodpecker 'creaked out the bass in the big dry trees. The weather was delightful and everything very pleasant'.

It was only a hasty memorandum of his observations for the day. Nevertheless, it was quite natural for Linnæus to let the woodpecker play the bass part in the orchestra. That is how he had heard it. He had listened to the bird-song as to a symphony. It was not a new literary affectation, for it was not literary, not intended for publication, and still less was it an affectation. But it was a new way of listening and feeling.

A fleeting sight, an everyday occurrence on the road, humble things and common objects were in his eyes great and noteworthy. He experienced everything with a remarkable intensity. Every judgment he made himself, every comparison he wrote down in his diary was a superlative.

On June 17th he saw

a number of cattle come running over the fields with the greatest velocity. Even the most miserably lean cows, which one would think scarcely able to drag one leg after another, went skipping along like does. They twisted their tails round and round, and went bounding and frisking about, till they at length reached a puddle, where they stopped all at once, as having found a sure asylum against the enemy that had put them to flight. Anxious to investigate what it could be that excited such extraordinary agitation, and prompted such exertions as neither the whip nor the fear of immediate death could occasion, I discovered it to be an insect which I had already met with lower down in the country, and which is no other than an *Oestrus* or Gadfly.

It is related in an old chronicle that when the King of Sweden in the 1580s, Johan III, lay dangerously ill at Drottningholm, he had helmets placed out in front of the deer in the park, who bounded past them, terrified; the king, it is said, grew mightily glad and merry at this deer-dance. The young Linnæus had only to see a prancing cow on his Lappland journey for his spirits to be exhilarated by the spectacle.

In Norway he fell in love. 'Here was a handsome daughter named Sara, eighteen years of age, uncommonly beautiful; must by and by be written to, for she is said never to believe that any honourable man shall come to her.'

Another time his raptures are called forth by the descent into a summer-decked valley after wandering on the mountain-tops:

When we at length arrived at the plains below, how grateful was the transition from a chill and frozen mountain to a warm balmy valley! I sat down to regale myself with wild strawberries. Instead of ice and snow, I was surrounded by vegetation in all its prime. Such tall grass I had never before beheld in any country. Instead of the blustering wind so lately experienced, soft breezes wafted around us the grateful scent of flowery clover and various other plants. *O formosissima æstas!*

O most delectable summer — one notices from the words how Linnæus revels in it with all his five senses.

In his cheerfulness of spirit, in his kindliness to all living creatures he even forgets his love of collecting occasionally for other feelings. He has not the heart to keep a captured ptarmigan fledgling:

The smaller ptarmigan . . . had their young. I took one, she (the mother) ran up to me, that I could have taken her, ran constantly round about me, so that 100 times I could have slain her without difficulty, had I not forborne to render the small nestlings defenceless at their tender age, and bethought me of the disposition of a mother's heart. I gave her back her son.

Brought to life by his imagination is *Andromeda polifolia*, growing in the marsh. The eminent authority on Linnæus, Felix Bryk, has gone so far as to consider the illustration of *Andromeda* drawn by Linnæus in his diary as a great work of art, worthy of a pre-Raphaelite painter and that only a pedant could criticize its technical immaturity. That is rather an overstatement. Linnæus was no artist with a drawing pen. But he was often an artist when he wrote, not least in his diary during his Lappland journey, and more particularly when he describes *Andromeda*:

The flowers are quite blood-red before they expand, but when full-grown the corolla is of a flesh-colour. Scarcely any painter's art can so happily imitate the beauty of a fine female complexion; still less could any artificial colour upon the face itself bear a comparison with this lovely blossom. As I contemplated it I could not help thinking of Andromeda as described by the poets; and the more I meditated upon their descriptions, the more applicable they seemed to the little plant before me, so that if these writers had had it in view, they could scarcely have contrived a more apposite fable. Andromeda is represented by them as a virgin of most exquisite and unrivalled charms; but these charms remain in perfection only so long as she retains her virgin purity, which is also applicable to the plant, now preparing to celebrate its nuptials. This plant is always fixed on some little turfy hillock in the midst of the swamps, as Andromeda herself was chained to a rock in the sea, which bathed her feet, as the fresh water does the roots of the plant. Dragons and venomous serpents surrounded her, as toads and other reptiles frequent the abode of her vegetable prototype, and, when they pair in the spring, throw mud and water over its leaves and branches. As the distressed virgin cast down her blushing face through excessive affliction, so does the rosy-coloured flower hang its head, growing paler and paler till it withers away.

In *Flora Lapponica* Linnæus was later to carry the comparison further between the Andromeda of mythology and the plant in the Lappland marshes, in a Latin that is more correct, more polished than the Swedish of the diary, but hardly as fresh. Especially to be noted is the logical sequence of the Linnean imagination; it is not enough that the plant is likened to the legendary maiden, but the frogs and toads spouting water in their mating antics are the counterparts to the poison-spitting dragons of mythology. It was a poet who wrote this, a poet in the first flush of youthful vigour.

* * *

It was also a happy young man. Things had indeed turned out well for him. The Society of Science's commission was flattering. The young Linnæus was to complete the work of the two Rudbecks. Who would dare compete with him among the other students? He had already done duty as Rudbeck's deputy. After the Lappland journey, when he had published his findings, when he had had time to arrange the new plants gathered each day by the wayside, by reindeer-tracks in the mountains, by mountain torrent and lakeshore, then surely

ANDROMEDA POLIFOLIA L. (life size).

'Dragons and venomous serpents surrounded her, as toads and other reptiles frequent the abode of her vegetable prototype . . . As the distressed virgin cast down her blushing face through excessive affliction, so does the rose-coloured flower hang its head.'

there was no doubt as to his being Rudbeck's successor. He had landed on his feet.

How unnecessary had been his parents' misgivings and anxiety! In very truth the stone rejected by the builder looked as though it were going to be a corner-stone. His mother may indeed have been most apprehensive of his perilous journey far up towards the Arctic Ocean. But she no longer spoke or even thought of the disappointment he had once occasioned her.

Many years later Carl's brother, Samuel Linnæus, in his account of Stenbrohult and the Linnæan family life previously quoted, related that there had been a great to-do in the vicarage beside Lake Möckeln when the son who was half regarded as a lost sheep had been made Rudbeck's deputy. 'Our late Mother's formerly cool feelings towards him now underwent a change. She saw her son as *vicarius professor*, so young. She was formerly of the mind that he could not become other than barber-surgeon: and instead she learnt that he was lecturing as professor, and that when hardly more than a second-year student. It was almost incredible.' And then his successes had followed on each other's heels. But the greatest hitherto was the commission to complete the work Rudbeck had left unfinished: the true discovery and description of Lappland.

No outsider knew, however, what great reason Linnæus had to feel illimitable joy when tracking down the fauna and flora of the far North. The manuscripts, notes, and drafts left in Upsala were the most important contributions made to the knowledge of the vegetable and animal kingdoms since the days of Aristotle. No one else knew this, but he himself was convinced of it. Within a few years he would not only be known in Upsala and approved of in Stenbrohult, he would be a world-famous man. His heart beat faster at the thought.

Linnæus was never happier than at this moment, in the midst of hardship and mischance in the wilds of Lappland. *A Tour in Lappland* is a document of his happiness.

But *A Tour in Lappland* not only shows how he could rejoice and experience delight. The diary also reveals how unstable his emotions were, how sensitive his feelings, how nervous and impatient his temperament.

In Jokkmokk he had fallen into dispute with two priests concerning certain meteorological matters. His two opponents get short shrift:

The clergyman, who is the schoolmaster, and the curate, tormented me with their consummate and most pertinacious ignorance. I could not but wonder how so much pride and ambition, such scandalous want of information, with such incorrigible stupidity, could exist in persons of their profession, who are commonly expected to be men of knowledge; yet any school-boy twelve years of age might be better informed. No man will deny the propriety of such people as these at least, being placed as far as possible from civilized society.

And this diatribe was not merely of the moment. In a survey, obviously written after his return, of the people he had met during his travels, the wretched curate, with his heretical views on meteorology, is described thus: 'A residuum, a brutal and illiterate man, regaled me most vulgarly with facetious insults. By their fruits shall ye know them.'

When Linnæus had taken a dislike it was not easily dispelled. It stuck fast. It was stubborn.

But without this quick temper his eye no doubt would have been less sharp. Had he been indifferent to anything, he would not have been the ardent soul he was, nor would his senses have been so alert. He would not then have described so tenderly and plastically the sight of a forest laid waste by fire:

I traversed a space three-quarters of a mile in extent which was entirely burnt, so that Flora, instead of appearing in her gay and verdant attire, was in deep sable, a spectacle more abhorrent to my feelings than to see her clad in the white livery of winter, for this, though it destroys the herbage, leaves the roots in safety, which the fire does not.

Nor would he, when he noticed a clicking noise from the reindeer's foot as it walked along, have immediately plunged into a speculative discussion concerning the cause.

Much on the journey he found odious and vile; by far the most was beautiful or curious; nothing was indifferent. On August 6th, which was a Sunday, he was in Torneå, and he notes in formal Latin that the day of the holy sabbath was devoted, as it should be, to recreation for both mind and body. Concerning the sermon, however, he has nothing to say; but in the church he found a memorial of King Charles XI's own observation of the sun on June 14th, 1694. He appears also to have closely observed the congregation, for he informs us that 'the wenches in Finland have bigger breasts than the girls in Lappland'. Nor had he forgotten the vicar on his return. In the list of his acquaintances in the North he mentions this worthy in the warmest terms, admiring his ability to preach in both Swedish and Finnish; he makes no mention, to be sure, of the drift of the vicar's sermon, but dwells at all the greater length on his excellent table. Linnæus delighted in the memory. He was not a gourmet, but he had keen senses.

And a brighter sensory pleasure than that reflected in *A Tour in Lappland* is unknown in Swedish literature.

*   *   *

Upon his return Linnæus wrote a shorter account of his journey for the benefit of the Society of Science, stating in one of his autobiographies that they were thereby well pleased. He himself was also well pleased. In this hastily written résumé he depicts Lappland as an earthly paradise, a land to which envy and money have not reached:

The many diseases which exercise their tyranny elsewhere, especially in the courts, do not intrude here until old age has gathered ripe fruit. Envy casts no jaundiced eye here. Neither has power over the next man any profit, nor does the nobleman hold any estate in demesne. The kings themselves do not disturb the people's peace with edicts and decrees, for mischief here has not begun to rebel. To drudge by the sweat of one's brow, which has made slaves of both high and low, is here unknown.

Words such as these, better than any utterance in *A Tour in Lappland*, might well serve as an instance of the thesis on

Linnæus's pre-Rousseauan pathos. But not even from them has one the right to draw such conclusions. Home again from his tour, with all hardships forgotten, Linnæus wrote his account in the best of spirits; he paid regard to the two Rudbecks' old dream of Atlantis, and out of politeness wrote in such a way that Rudbeck the younger might well be satisfied. He himself, now that all was overcome, understood the call of the wild, and for this fascination he could find no other words than those used by Ovid and Virgil when speaking of the golden age, the age of innocence.

It is well known that when the men who had drawn up the map of Africa or Asia — in the days when there were still regions to be mapped — came home again, they always wrote accounts of their vicissitudes and adventures in such a way that the reader, while yet commiserating with them in their perilous travels, was left with a longing for the fate that had been theirs, a longing to see undiscovered lands, for virgin territory, for visions of the world as it was in the dawn of creation. When Linnæus came home with his Lapp drum and Lappland dress he felt like Marco Polo. And as a Marco Polo he was treated up to a point in Sweden, but most particularly so abroad.

During his stay in foreign parts some years later, when in quick succession he wrote the books on which his scientific fame is based, it meant much to him that a learned Dutch society wished to see him in his Lappland dress. He could freely profit from the glamour pertaining to an explorer. He had himself painted in Lappland costume. He even made no bones about magnifying his exploration when the occasion offered. When he had published *Critica Botanica* he wrote to Haller, his great rival in the field of natural science, that any shortcomings in the Latin should be overlooked, since 'intercourse with Lapps, Finns and Norwegians, during several years, has made me more barbarous than Michele'. This Michele was in his time a well-known botanist; clearly his Latin was not considered classical. But Linnæus's statement that his breach of Latin syntax was due to his having been isolated for years with Lapps, Finns, and Norwegians, does show that he did not exactly minimize the remarkable fact of his Lappland journey when associating with foreigners. It shows something else too: that Linnæus spoke and wrote in superlatives; that his writings must be read with a sense for his personal value of the words.

*   *   *

Linnæus did not publish the scientific results of his Lappland expedition until 1737, during his sojourn in Holland, in his book *Flora Lapponica*. The book is arranged as a plant index; the plants found in Lappland are listed in accordance with their sexual system. But it is a comprehensive catalogue; none of Linnæus's scientific Latin works has greater literary merit. It is patent that Linnæus this time has also taken great pains with the form of the book. The text bristles with Latin quotations, mostly from Virgil and Ovid, and the classical allusions are numerous. It may also be remarked that the get-up of the book was in excellent taste; the plant reproductions in the first edition are a joy to behold. As the author himself says in the preface: this is a Flora 'decked in festal attire'.

To his plant classifications Linnæus has attached historical and cultural, zoological, and ethnographical notes and descriptions, sometimes, too, accounts, often graphic and charming, of how the finds occurred. He tells of a species of Andromeda, not that recently mentioned, but the one known as *Cassiope tetragona*, which he found on Mount Vallivari in Lappland:

Whilst I was walking quickly along, in a profuse perspiration, facing the cold wind, at midnight— if I may call it night when the sun shone without setting at all— still anxiously inquiring of my interpreter how near we were to a Lappland dwelling, which I had for two hours been expecting, though I knew not its precise situation, casting my eager eyes around me in all directions, I perceived as it were the shadow of this plant, but did not then stop to examine it. After going a few steps further, however, an idea of its being something I was unacquainted with came across my mind, and I turned back. I know not what it is that so deceives the sight in our Alps during the night, as to render objects far less distinct than in the middle of the day, though the sun shines equally bright. The sun being near the horizon, spreads its rays in such a horizontal direction, that a hat can scarcely protect our eyes: besides, the shadows of plants are so infinitely extended, and so confounded with each other, from the tremulous agitation caused by the blustering wind, that objects very different in themselves are scarcely to be distinguished from each other.

This passage may be quoted as proof of how concrete this plant catalogue is. And how extraordinarily true to life is the description of the strange dreamy radiance of the limpid mountain night!

Another time it is childhood memories from Stenbrohult that are wakened to life by the finding of a plant. Even in this account, intended for the world of learned men, Linnæus does not fight shy of weaving autobiographical details into the text and lauding his dear birthplace. Up in the Norwegian Finnmark he had found *Narthecium ossifragum*. Immediately he tells us:

In the Swedish province of Småland and the parish of Stenbrohult situated therein, far indeed from Norway, this plant flourishes in the greatest profusion, its comely flowers having often attracted my gaze. It was spoken of so much that even as a boy I heard innumerable tales concerning it from the peasantry. There was not one to whom it was not thoroughly familiar. It was there called *ilar*-wort and everyone asserted unanimously that it was a plant noxious to sheep in the highest degree. If they ate thereof in abundance, they became fat very quickly, but the very next year they would certainly die, having engendered in their livers small worms, called *ilar*, hence the name of the plant.

When Linnæus describes bilberries, he gives a detailed account of a Lapplandic cheese dish in which these berries are used, and also gives a magnificent description of the mass of capercaillie, black-cock, hazel-hen, and ptarmigan which eat bilberries, not only in the autumn but well into the winter, when the berries have already withered. The path he treads is often far from his starting-point. When he deals with the

Lappland fungi, he states that mushrooms, called by the Greeks ambrosia, are in Sweden only held to be a *délice* by foreigners; with us the choicest serve as sustenance for the flies; and so Linnæus is led on to the subject of different kinds of flies and gadflies; and thence to the annoyance which the gadflies cause the reindeer herds — a subject he greatly puzzled over and was to deal with separately some years later; finally the thought strikes him that flies who persecute the reindeer resemble persistent suitors, and he concludes in the following original manner:

The egg-filled gadfly all day long pursues the reindeer over mountain and steep, valley and fell, striving always to lay its eggs on the reindeer's back. And that he may not succumb to the cold in these chilly mountainous regions the Creator has clad him entirely with hair. The reindeer, on the other hand, even if a thousand are gathered in a single herd, kick, snort, and ceaselessly fling their bodies hither and thither, if but one such weak defenceless little fly buzzes over them, and they do not cease to do this for one second, until it has disappeared, so that, if perchance an egg has fallen on their back, it may soon be shaken off. All day long in the summer they roam on the perpetually snow-clad fells and, if they wander about without a tender, they always rush at full speed into the wind, that no such fly may follow them. They scarcely dare to graze all the warm day long, but are on the alert with watchful eyes and pricked-up ears in case such a fly should be in the vicinity. The fly, however, pursues them to the limit of its strength, and then often falls down on to the very snow from exhaustion. When it has rested there, it seeks if possible to find a green spot, and — soon its desire is aroused to seek out again the object of its longing. O, with what a variety of arrows Cupid inflicts his wounds! How different, and yet the same as of yore, are the effects of these, as is to be read in the lines of Ovid, Metamorphoses I. line 468:

There, from his quiver's abundant store he chose two darts, of widely different kind: one kindles love, the other puts it to flight.

The one which kindles love is of gold with a sharp point; The one which puts to flight is blunt and dipped in lead.

It may be wondered whether the god of love and the Roman poet's description of his arrows have ever figured in a more curious context. It is no far-fetched comparison concocted at a writing-desk. One can see how it has come about. Linnæus has had Cupid and Ovid in his mind during his Lappland journey when he saw the gadfly chase the reindeer herds. And when composing his scientific report he could not bring himself to suppress his fanciful idea or to stem the swift flow of his imaginary associations. He must have smiled when he wrote these Latin sentences.

It is not the only time he smiles in *Flora Lapponica*. There is a somewhat similar turn of phrase in another account of fungi:

The Lappland youth, having found this mushroom, carefully preserves it in a little pocket hanging at his waist, that its grateful perfume may render him more acceptable to his favourite fair one. O whimsical Venus! In other regions you must be treated with coffee and chocolate, preserves and sweetmeats, wines and dainties, jewels and pearls, gold and silver, silks and cosmetics, balls and assemblies, music and theatrical exhibitions: here you are satisfied with a little withered fungus!

Thus was the language of learning fashioned by the young explorer. It is perhaps not surprising that among his audience — the grave botanists and natural scientists of England and the Continent — there were those who shook their heads. Was not this tone in itself testimony that the lewd sexual system involved the most dangerous consequences? In fact, it is remarkable that not more grizzled and arid heads irately tossed their dusty wigs.

CAROLI LINNÆI

Naturæ Curioſorum *Dioſcoridis Secundi*

SYSTEMA
NATURÆ

IN QUO

NATURÆ REGNA TRIA,

SECUNDUM

CLASSES, ORDINES, GENERA, SPECIES,

SYSTEMATICE PROPONUNTUR.

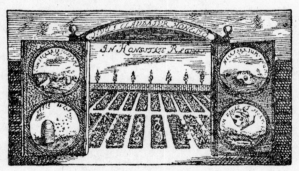

Editio Secunda, Auctior.

STOCKHOLMIÆ
Apud GOTTFR. KIESEWETTER.
1740.

Frontispiece of *Systema Naturæ*, Second Edition

CHAPTER V

SYSTEMA NATURÆ

DURING the years following his expedition to Lappland Linnæus journeyed far and wide. It was clear that travelling appealed to him, not so much for the sake of change and enjoyment as for the purpose of study and discovery. Both in 1733 and 1734 he moved about in Bergslagen and Dalarna, and his descriptions of these tours have as great a factual interest as the Lappland journey, if not quite the same poetic charm. In Old Testament style he sings of the wonders he beheld:

Almighty Creator and Preserver of all things, who hast
in the Lappland fells suffered me to come so high up,
in the Falun mine suffered me to come so deep down,
in the Lappland fells shown me *diem sine nocte*, day without
     night,
in the Falun mine shown me *noctem sine die*, night without day,
in the Lappland fells suffered me to be where cold is never
     ending,
in the Falun mine suffered me to be where heat is never
     ending,
in the Lappland fells suffered me in one place to see all the
     world's 4 seasons,
in the Falun mine suffered me in one place to see not one of
     the 4 seasons,
in Lappland led me unharmed through so many mortal
     dangers,
in Falun Bergslag led me unharmed through so many perils
     to health,
praised be all Thou hast created
from the beginning to the end.

In this prose poem there is a strong poetic feeling for the strangeness of his own destiny and his own impressions, mingled with genuine piety. Perhaps one can also detect another trait, less laudable. In Bergslagen Linnæus made a study of mineralogy, partly as a means of support; in Upsala he gave lessons in the art of assaying. His mineralogical studies resulted in a thesis called *Pluto Svecicus*; in passing it should be pointed out that his naively sensuous imagination was always looking for mythological symbols; a thesis on our mineral springs begun about the same time he had thought of entitling *Naiades Svecicæ*; the art of assaying he saw as the Pluto of the ancients, and those who took the waters led his thoughts to the wet, gleaming bodies of the Naiads; he was an aesthete. The mineralogical manuscript containing his experiments concerning the different kinds of minerals was not published until 1907, and the prominent expert responsible for editing it writes in the introduction:

Characteristic of *Pluto Svecicus* are the superlative expressions occurring here and there, which may not exclusively be ascribed to the Roman language. For instance, we read '*Ambra est omnium lapidum suaveolentissimus*' (of all stones ambra is the smoothest); '*praetiosissimus*' (the most costly of all). Presumably these and similar expressions were justified at that time, but they make one think of a language very different from Latin. An expression such as 'the biggest in the world' tells us where the present-day equivalent is to be found. There is in Linné something of the genuine and best American pioneer spirit: energy and masterliness confronted with vast virgin territories. The State boundaries or the town plan of New York could not have been laid out in more rectilinear co-ordinates than those of *Regnum lapidum*, the mineral kingdom. We find here the real American striving after easily accessible order and perspicuity, not seldom at the expense of thoroughness; the enumeration of the stone specimens in *Pluto Svecicus* has almost the character of book-keeping, and we are scarcely surprised at finding the long list of rock specimens on page 43 begin with the words 'brought forward'.

The only fault to be found with this very valuable and perspicacious statement by an eminent specialist is that Linnæus had nothing whatever to do with American mentality; but he did rush along with brilliant impetuosity over ground he had not managed to explore properly, and he did feel the poet's need to magnify: to magnify observations, magnify the importance of noted continuity of thought, magnify his own emotions, magnify the virtues and vices of his friends and enemies.

Elias Fries, who alone among the Swedish natural scientists after Linnæus also had a mastery of the *humaniora* of his age, wrote as early as 1848, troubled by the way the Linnean history-writing had developed:

In Linné's personal account of his life, as well as in recorded tradition, a magnifying power of imagination has attached importance to the external and inessential, more to the world of flowers outside him than to his own inner life.

And to this Elias Fries added a note as follows:

Hence the exaggeration of Linné's small youthful reverses, in the account of *Furia Infernalis*, of persecutions and then all the small distinctions, etc. Who can now find any low intrigue in the fact that the associate professor of medicine returning from abroad was appointed to lecture in Rudbeck's place before the student Linné.

The biographical fact Fries hints at here has given rise to copious scribbling in literature concerning Linnæus. The matter was like this: Linnæus, who for a time had upheld the appointment as lecturer within the medical faculty, was eliminated in the academic competition by a highly qualified rival, Rosén, afterwards Rosenstein, one of Sweden's greatest medical men. Linnæus was beside himself with fury. He behaved as Swedish academicians usually do in such situations, and became thoroughly put out and peevish. What needs to be explained and defended here is simply this, that the young eagle started cheeping as though he were the common sparrow's cousin.

Uggla, during his profitable study of the Linnean Society's collection of manuscripts, has found the draft of a letter from the twenty-five-year-old Linnæus to one of the greatest contemporary botanists, Professor Dillenius of Oxford. It was probably written at the beginning of 1733; it is not definitely known whether it was ever sent.

In the letter the Swedish medical student, with typically youthful lack of diffidence, gives an account of his scientific merits; amongst other things he expresses his conviction that Dillenius would find great pleasure in reading his work in manuscript form, *Fundamenta Botanica*, before publishing the large-scale botanical work he was planning. Concerning his rivalry with Rosén he writes as follows:

During this year I have acquired a rival, associate professor in the faculty, my bitter foe, who has succeeded in having the public lectures made over to him, although in natural history he is as a donkey with a zither. It is the ordinary Swedish envy!

Yes, it was the ordinary Swedish envy, though not as Linnæus would have us think. But how had Linnæus come to be so ordinary? It seems to me, however, that in his defence one may plead a circumstance which to a certain extent explains his attitude on this occasion.

What all this meant to Linnæus — to be able suddenly, as a young student, to lecture in Rudbeck's place — is apparent from the account already quoted by his brother Samuel, vicar of Stenbrohult, of the flutter in the nest when the son, who was considered half lost, was made Rudbeck's deputy overnight: 'Our late Mother's formerly cool feelings towards him now underwent a change.'

This passage is important to the understanding of Linnæus. It must first be realized that his mother's lack of faith in his capabilities had long depressed him, a feeling no doubt shared by himself too in his sombre moments. Then suddenly came the appointment to take charge of the botanical demonstrations, accompanied by a complete reversal of his mother's attitude. And when, equally unexpectedly, the appointment ceased, Linnæus must have been concerned as to how this set-back would be viewed by his mother at home in Stenbrohult; she died in the summer of 1733.

It was not to be wondered at that he was unable to judge the circumstances fairly and dispassionately. Not merely for the sake of his own self-esteem, but also because of his mother's mistrust, he had to cling to the fiction of persecution, to the accusation of Swedish envy.

If one bears this state of affairs in mind, what appears offensive in the letter to Dillenius is no longer quite so objectionable. The young Linnæus had good reason, not objective but strongly subjective, to feel for the time being like Aladdin robbed of lamp and castle by a wicked magician. One can hardly expect Aladdin in this situation to behave in a well-balanced and unassuming manner.

There is, however, still another reason for these indications of over-sensitiveness during this period. He is the greatest theoretical genius our country has produced, but nothing in his phenomenal career is more phenomenal than his work during his student years. Until the vast collection of youthful Linnean manuscripts preserved by the Linnean Society in London has been thoroughly examined and dated, no precise knowledge can be had as to the extent of his output during those early years. So much is plain, however, that in the autumn of 1733 Linnæus had clearly in his head the theories which, put into print in Holland, were to make him world-famous. In a letter written in October of this year he enumerates a long list of scientific works he is planning; the entire ground-plan of his life's work is clear. Within both botany and zoology the brown-eyed student had, independently and apart from his other occupations, basically changed the direction and method of research.

If one considers its far-reaching results, his work may be reckoned as our country's greatest scientific achievement. The list mentioned above is as follows (and let us when reading the often curious style remember that these works, indicated in Latin and briefly outlined, were soon to become completed theses, with which modern natural science has not yet settled its account):

As fruits I can show the following volumes in M.s.s. elaborated by me *propria Minerva*, such as:

1) *Bibliotheca Botanica*, which reviews all botanical books, ranged in natural order; all *methodicorum asseclæ* under their *primores*.

2) *Systemata Botanica*, in which all *botanicorum teorie* are shown in *compendio*.

3) *Philosophia Botanica*, where all *botanici* have not possessed more than 20 to 30 general principles, I have brought them by means of an unbelievable autopsy to between 200 and 400. Showing first, how he and she in the plant world conceive in almost the same manner as with animals. From which one should know all plants at a glance; wherein *botanici* are deceived when they have made absurd new systems.

4) *Harmonymia Botanica* shows how all plant names should be made, that not one tenth part of all *nomina generica* are correct, and that no *nom. specificum* is rightly done; how they should be done.

5) *Characteres Generici*, to know all plants at a glance, through the flower's definition, is here demonstrated in a practical manner. And that these could be applied to all methods which are made or can be made; this no *botanicus* has understood.

6) *Species Plantarum* under their *genera*.

7) *Species Plantarum, Tomus alter*.

8) *Nuptiæ Plantarum*. No Swede has yet made any method, but abroad commonly one in each kingdom, for this is the greatest art in botany. For I have done this from a new *principio*, where all others are from a false one, but mine is now being printed in Germany.

9) *Adonis Uplandicus*, all the garden plants in Upland described for the students, also sent away to be printed.

10) *Flora Lapponica* describes the plants and trees which grow in Lappland, so thoroughly that all *fungi* and *musci* are dealt with, together with their virtues and use by the Lapps, with illustrations and descriptions of more than 100 rare plants almost never seen, much less ever described heretofore.

11) *Lachesis Lapponica* indicates Lappland's physical characteristics and economy, costumes, hunting, etc., in Swedish.

12) *Aves Svecicæ*, describes over 300 species of birds observed in Sweden, and teaches how to know them at a glance.

13) *Insecta Uplandica* describes 1200 insects in Upland, observed, collected and still preserved by me.

Plus numerous additions.

What, then, did the recipient of this letter think as he read it? Probably just that *studiosus* Linnæus did not hide his light under a bushel. He no doubt shook his head, little dreaming that this letter, which sounded so boastful, was no more than a catologue. Obviously Linnæus had in his possession the finished or half-finished manuscripts of a good many of his subsequently classical works on Flora and Fauna.

*   *   *

During the year 1735 Linnæus made a number of notes in his diary which enable us to keep track of him. When the church bells rang in the New Year he was in Falun, and on the second day of the year he paid his court, clad in his famous and very striking Lappland dress, to one of the town's richest heiresses, the eighteen-year-old Sara Lisa, daughter of Johan Moræus, M.D., a man of magnificence. What the suitor from Upsala looked for in the fair sex was first and foremost a respectable dowry, then a smooth, firm flesh, and lastly a supple disposition. He had stated this many times, and his robust declarations give a certain twist of comedy to the romantic embellishments posterity has woven on the theme. Linnæus made a good bargain; the girl's money was secure, her person was pretty enough, and that she would become both miserly and ill-tempered in her middle age it was impossible to foresee. Especially significant was the fact that Doctor Moræus seems to have ruled quite forcibly that his future son-in-law, to be fully acceptable, must journey to Holland and there acquire a doctor's diploma.

What Linnæus saw abroad has been related by his biographers. He himself has been more reticent. The account of his travels which he began, *Iter ad Exteros*, leaves off before he has reached his destination. But the great cultural interest his visit to Holland may possess has no corresponding point in the story of his mental development. As he rode southwards a box chock-full of manuscripts hung on one side of his saddle. He published *Systema Naturæ* in Holland, but the system was ready before he left Upsala. I shall try to give an idea of its meaning.

In the matter of plants Linnæus, while still in his early twenties, had already made the observations concerning the determination of sex which form the basis of his system. From the very beginning he had realized that this system was artificial; but he also saw that this artificial division at once meant that there was order in a world hitherto seemingly chaotic. His lyrical delight in the description of the sexuality of plants is at bottom due to the fact that his need for clarity, his desire to find the pattern in the loom of cause and effect, had thereby been satisfied. Each flower in itself was indeed beautiful to behold; but in the plants' systematism Linnæus saw the hand of God in the world He had created.

It is not so easy for us today to realize just what Linnæus thought, felt and had in mind as he groped his way forward to a systematic classification within botany, zoology, and mineralogy. We must try to forget our modern knowledge, and with the help of our imagination attempt to follow Linnæus's gropings when these sciences were in their infancy.

I shall endeavour to make the matter as concrete as possible. I am sitting glancing through a large book called *A Monograph of the Turdidæ*, an almost complete account of all the different species of thrushes to be found in the world, a gigantic work by the great English ornithologist, Henry Seebohm. One can be quite sure that Linnæus would have been overjoyed if he could see this book; he would be delighted by the magnificent pictures, the extensive information regarding habitat and the exact and detailed description of species; he would even have been able to assert, with complete justification, that the publication of such a book had been made possible by his own life's work; it is the Linnean tradition of a 'family' system which is still carried on today as evidenced by these mighty volumes on the thrush.

Thus far would we and Linnæus be of one mind. But in the matter of what is most essential we should not speak the same language. Of whatever faith he may be, how does a present-day reader approach a zoological work based on the family system? If he is a Darwinian, he has in mind nature's adaptability and seeks the connection between the plumage of different species of thrush and their environment in different quarters of the globe; if he is a Mendelian his interest may be concentrated more on mutation. But whatever his biological tenet, he will be certain that the mutual resemblance of all the different species of thrush and the similarity in their bodily structure and plumage is due to their having a common origin. With all their variations they reveal, to his eyes, a common pedigree. They have become perfected and altered during geological eras for one reason or another; but he takes it for granted that the resemblance is due to a common origin. He cannot help being influenced by the theory of evolution. He must always presuppose an ever continuous transformation. The conception of a species is not a constant factor for him. A Peruvian thrush differs from a Brazilian thrush, either because the genus has in both cases adapted itself to different surroundings or because certain mutations have arisen within one or the other of the species.

But in order to understand Linnæus we must first and foremost try to forget these later developments of knowledge. When Linnæus grouped species and genera, genera and classes, he had not the slightest thought of a genetic connection, of heredity and development. For Linnæus and his age all species were settled once and for all, created by God in the dawn of time. The classification into biological groups therefore meant something entirely different to Linnæus from what it does to us. It meant that God, like a skilful weaver with warp and woof, produced a clear and lovely pattern, so arranged and fashioned in the natural objects, zoological, botanical, and mineral, that a definite scheme must be apparent to the beholder. In this world of nature, defined for all time, there is a plan, a geometrical tendency. Nature has received from the Lord of Creation the impulse to arrange itself in certain forms. The species were, to Linnæus, ideas that existed in God's consciousness before there was any creation. To find resemblances and connections, therefore, was not for Linnæus what it is for us, i.e. to establish a small part of infinitely composite development, but instead to find in nature itself the traces of God's own plan of creation.

Often quoted are the lines which the ageing Linnæus wrote of himself and his life's work:

God has suffered him to peep into his secret cabinet. God has suffered him to see more of his created work than any mortal before him. God has endowed him with the greatest insight into natural knowledge, greater than any has ever gained. The Lord has been with him, whithersoever he has gone, and has exterminated all his enemies for him, and has made of him a great name, as one of the great ones of the earth.

To speak of oneself in this biblical style points undeniably to a strongly developed sense of one's own importance. But it is easier to understand how Linnæus has come to think in this way if one considers the difference between the conception of nature in his age and ours. For Linnæus the system of nature meant, in a nutshell, God's eternal design. Like Faust he had caught sight of the signs of the Macrocosm:

How all things weave themselves into a unity,
One thing living within the other!
How heavenly powers move up and down
passing golden pails to one another!

It was in Holland in 1735, at the age of twenty-eight, that Linnæus published the first edition of *Systema Naturæ*. The book comprises only ten or so folio pages, admittedly very large and comprehensive. On two pages the minerals, on three pages the plants, and on two pages the animals — from human beings to worms — have been systematically arranged according to species. What Linnæus considered he had found was simply the plan of creation. Even the artificial classification — monandria, diandria, triandria, etc. — had the same deep significance for him.

It has been questioned whether Linnæus was in the main scientifically, aesthetically, or religiously inclined. This question is rather pointless inasmuch as abstract systematic thought, to the young Linnæus at least, had an affinity with sensuous observation; he saw his system, and was delighted aesthetically by its clarity. Nor did he doubt for a moment that it was through the especial dispensation of Providence that he had been chosen to discover the coherence of existence, the affinity of the species, this order, this connecting link which to him was the expression of God's entity: *ens entium*.

In one of the later editions of *Systema Naturæ* — when the book had swollen to a vast catalogue of all the plant and animal species known to Linnæus — it is stated in the preface: The purpose of the earth's creation is God's teaching, apparent through the works of nature, interpreted by man alone — *Finis Creationis telluris est gloria Dei ex opere Naturæ per Hominem solum.*

Linnæus thought from time to time that he was the only one who had been able correctly to execute this interpretation. His *Systema Naturæ* was a world doctrine.

It has a certain resemblance to Mohammed's claim: there is no God other than nature and Linnæus is his prophet.

*   *   *

It is well known how the young Swede entered the service of the rich Clifford. Linnæus has described the garden at Hartecamp in the dedication to Clifford with which he begins the great work *Hortus Cliffortianus*, wherein he describes scientifically the mass of exotic plants gathered there from the four corners of the earth. It is an usually magnificent volume, whose exquisite engravings can never fail to send even the most fastidious booklover into raptures.

CARL LINNÆUS

My eyes [Linnæus writes in the preface] were ravished on the
instant by so many masterpieces of nature, aided by art,
walks, beds, statues, artificial lakes and artistically built slopes
and mazes. I was entranced by your menageries, full of tigers,
monkeys, wild dogs, Indian deer and goats, South American
and African swine; mixed with their cries were those of flocks
of birds: American falcons, divers kinds of parrots, pheasants,
peacocks, guinea-fowl, American capercaillie, Indian hens,
swans, many different kinds of ducks and geese, gulls and
other web-footed birds, snipe, American crossbills, sparrows
of divers kinds, turtle-doves and other doves together with
various other species of birds, with whose cries the garden
resounded.

Although this dedication is written in the true Latin style,
which in keeping with the demands of the occasion had something of the ceremonious air of court dress, it is not difficult
to discern, behind the enumeration of all the rarities, the
author's enthusiasm over the wealth of nature that surrounded
him. The woods of Stenbrohult, as he tells us in his fragmentary *Iter ad Exteros*, had indeed sounded 'like a paradise
of birds'; the cries emanating from the cages in Clifford's park
were no doubt far less delightful, but the cages contained new,
unknown birds, which were to have their place in his natural
system. And still more numerous were the wonders in the
greenhouses. Linnæus continues:

I was greatly amazed when I entered the greenhouses, full as
they were of so many plants that a son of the North must feel
bewitched, and wonder to what strange quarter of the globe he
had been transported. In the first house were cultivated an
abundance of flowers from southern Europe, plants from
Spain, the South of France, Italy, Sicily, and the isles of
Greece. In the second were treasures from Asia, such as
Poincianas, cocoanut and other palms, etc.; in the third, Africa's
strangely shaped, not to say misshapen plants, such as the
numerous forms of the Aloe and Mesembryanthemum
families, carnivorous flowers, Euphorbias, Crassula and
Protea species, and so on. And finally in the fourth green-
house were grown the charming inhabitants of America and

the rest of the New World; large masses of Cactus varieties, orchids, cruciferæ, yams, magnolias, tulip-trees, calabash trees, arrow, cassias, acacias, tamarinds, pepper-plants, Anona, manicinilla, cucurbitaceous trees and many others, and, surrounded by these, plantains, the most stately of all the world's plants, the most beauteous Hernandia, silver-gleaming species of Protea and camphor-trees. When I then entered the positively royal residence and the extremely instructive museum, whose collections no less spoke in their owner's praise, I, a stranger, felt completely enraptured, as I had never before seen its like. My heart-felt wish was that I might lend a helping hand with its management.

The most distinguished achievement of the 'helping hand' turned out to be *Hortus Cliffortianus*, which claimed most of his time during his stay in Hartecamp. But he was young and happy and inspired, and in the evenings he wrote (according to his own account in order to 'amuse himself') another work, in which he explained and defended the new botanical terminology he put into practice in *Hortus Cliffortianus*. It was *Critica Botanica*, a book that has much to tell the present-day reader about the whole world of Linnæus's ideas and about his personality.   *   *   *

As is known, Linnæus did not manage to bring about the binominal nomenclature, now to be found in every flora, until the 1750s, when he published his main botanical work, *Species Plantarum*. In his youthful work, *Critica Botanica*, he only managed to set forth the general principles for the nomenclature. He takes as his starting-point a saying of Isidorus: 'If one does not know the names, one's knowledge of things is useless.' Nomenclature is, he says, equally important in botany as classification. But before such a nomenclature can be generally achieved one must be agreed as to the basis on which it is to be undertaken.

Linnæus demands first and foremost that the family names shall be uniform, i.e. that species belonging to the same family shall have the same family designation. To us this seems quite obvious, but at that time it was neither acknowledged nor even conceived. Similarly, he requires that similar family names shall not be used in regard to species belonging to separate families. To this, too, the same applies as to Columbus's egg. The plant names before Linnæus's time were a jumbled, incoherent mass.

A writer on the history of culture who reads *Critica Botanica* may, it is true, sometimes think that Linnæus is a trifle drastic. Linnæus is quite willing to accept the ancient Greek and Latin denominations, but he puts his pen vigorously through almost all the old medieval designations that are so full of atmosphere. He decrees sharply:

We revere the Creator's omnipotence and the sublime secrets he manifests in the plants; but we do not allow the use of such names as have a religious significance.

Roma locuta est. Thus at Linnæus's command there vanished the old plant names that had derived from monastery gardens, names like *Paternoster, Gratia Dei, Oculus Christi, Spina Christi.* Even in English these names sound attractive: Our Father, the Grace of God, the Eye of Christ, the Thorn of Christ. But Linnæus had not much feeling for such romantic ideas. He desired clarity and universal applicability. With all his mysticism he was first and foremost a rationalist. And as I have pointed out in another context, the old medieval herbal knowledge with all its poetical names had a very utilitarian purpose; the monastic nomenclature Linnæus associated not with vespers and the Angelus and the sound of bells, but with apothecaries. This should be borne in mind when reading *Critica Botanica.*

On the other hand, Linnæus writes that 'family names created in order to preserve the memory of a botanist who has shown himself deserving of science I hold with as a religious duty'. In the development of this thesis, already established in *Fundamenta Botanica* (generally speaking the whole of *Critica Botanica* is a continuous commentary on the theses in *Fundamenta Botanica*) Linnæus reveals much of his innermost convictions and thoughts at this time.

It may well be thought, Linnæus points out, that name and plant should be as closely united as possible; therefore names of famous botanists are not suitable, as between them and the plant as such there cannot be any resemblance. But to this his reply is that if one examines the family names one finds among them scarcely one out of fifty containing something characteristic of the species the family embraces. It does not much matter where the family name is taken from. What has Anglia to do with angels? Must a person whose name is Peter be hard as stone?

Moreover, Linnæus continues, it is apparent to anyone versed in botanical literature that there is a link connecting the botanist's name with the plant called after him, and 'in this association there is a gratification which prevents it from being effaced from the memory'. Whereupon follows a catalogue of plants named after botanists. It could not have been compiled by anyone other than Linnæus; it is altogether delightful in its mixture of politeness and malice, humour and irony, subtlety and winsomeness. One or two samples may be quoted:

Pisonia is a tree of sombre appearance, owing to its thorns — according to a tradition concerning Piso, who is in very truth sombre, if what a relation of Marcgraf accuses him of is true, namely that he got all his knowledge from Marcgraf after the latter's death, etc. See and compare for yourself the imputations; compare also Marcgraf's writings with Piso's.

Commelina has flowers with three petals, of which two are distinct but the third hardly conspicuous; after the two botanists whose name was Commelin: for the third died before he achieved anything in botany.

Dorstenia, whose flowers have little to show, as though they were withered and had seen their best days, recalls Dorsten's work to mind.

Hernandia is an American tree, with more beautiful leaves than anything else, but with less notable flowers — after a botanist who had extraordinarily good luck and who was highly paid for his research into American natural history: if only the fruits of his labours had equalled the expenditure!

Dillenia has the most magnificent flower and fruit of all plants, just as Dillenius is a magnificent specimen among botanists.
Gronovia is a creeper, which embraces all other plants within reach, called after a man who has few equals as an embracer and collector of plants (Gronovius).
Linnea was no doubt given its name by Gronovius and is a plant in Lappland, of short growth, insignificant, overlooked, flowering only a very short time; the plant is called after Linnæus, who resembles it.

This, written by a thirty-year-old who only a few years previously was an undergraduate at Upsala, is superbly done. It must be admitted, however, that the explanation Linnæus gives of a number of plant names implies rather a perpetual sneer at the botanists after whom they are called. Even Gronovius, who was so close to Linnæus, who rendered him untold services and for whom nothing was too much trouble, seems here to be moved down to the collector's unpretentious class. That Linnæus also speaks of himself in unassuming terms is, in the circumstances, the least one could expect.

However, as soon as this was committed to paper he seems to have felt that some addition was called for, that the botanists were deserving of a laudatory word without any critical reservations. He therefore continues by writing a memorial in honour of the botanists in splendidly rhetorical style. And this is typical of his mentality; it is as though he immediately regretted the derogatory judgments he had passed, and began to fear he had committed an injustice both to other botanists and to himself. His emotional life was intense and unstable.

Have not many islands got their names from their European discoverers, he asks. Has not one quarter of the globe been called after 'the insignificant example of the human race' called Amerigo? And is it not right, therefore, Linnæus wonders, when for want of better family names a plant family is named after its discoverer?

What can mortals desire more in this transient world of little moment, [he continues] than that a creditable memory of

LINNÆA BOREALIS L. (life size).

LINNEA

'. . . a plant in Lappland, of short growth, insignificant, overlooked, flowering only a very short time; the plant is called after Linnæus, who resembles it.'

their names may reach posterity and live yet a few days more. How many heroes, how many kings and emperors, how many valiant and intrepid men have not offered themselves to Bellona in order that their names might become a legend for posterity? [And, he asks, why should this not also apply to botanists, 'whose adventures have been equally bold' . . .]

Then follows a brilliant tirade:

What pains, what research could be more tiring and laborious than botany, if it were not that the enchantment of a strange will, which I myself cannot explain, often drove us in this direction, so that love of plants vanquishes love of ourselves? Good God! When I muse upon the fate of botanists, upon my word I know not whether I shall call them wise or bereft of reason in their enthusiasm for plants. I shall merely add one or two examples.
In my youth I penetrated into the wilds of Lappland, although I was familiar neither with the language of the Lapps nor their customs and way of living. I lived solely on water and meat, without bread or salt: I risked my life on the mountain of Skulberget in Finnmark, on the alpine glaciers, or by ship-wreck, or amidst the clouds; wandering on foot I forced my way through forests and mountainous regions, and all this with the aim of collecting plants belonging to the meagre Lappland Flora.

One notices that the perils of the Lappland journey have not paled in his memory with the years. But having first set a wreath of laurels on his own head he proceeds to distribute the same honour to a long line of other botanists:

Hermann, after having completed journeys in Africa and Ceylon, gets bronchitis through living in his garden in the wintertime and thinking more of his plants than of his health, and dies.

He mentions many cases of a like nature.

Oldenland makes the strange plants of the Cape of Good Hope known to his own country, and dies out there as a result of change of climate. Barrelier got asthma through his botanical journeys and died of it. Marcgravius, not content with his

American trophies, seeks also to exhaust Africa, where he perishes. Lippi (Augustus) prefers a journey to Egypt and Ethiopia to a doctor's degree, and is tragically stabbed by robbers in Abyssinia and perishes.

When Linnæus speaks of these and other similar destinies, we of a later age can see these epitaphs in the light of prophecies as well. To the same starvation, to the same struggle, to the same death were his pupils to go.

He also names other tribulations, other tests of steadfastness. 'Rudbeck (Olof, the father), a man of steadfast disposition, saw twelve volumes of *Campi Elysii*, on which he had long been working, consumed by fire, slowly pines away and dies of a broken heart.' He also pays tribute here to his foremost teachers in botany: Tournefort, whose travels in Europe and in the Orient he honours in pompous phrases, and Vaillant, who died of a disease contracted while studying bogs.

Then comes the finale. He wants to finish by enumerating examples. Every botanist knows himself 'how many laborious days and sleepless nights, how many hours which it was difficult to spare from other occupations, and what enormous sums he has sacrificed, merely with the intention of serving others'. The honour botanists acquire through plants being called after them can never be too great, rather the reverse:

Alas that so much toil should gain so humble a reward; and yet how welcome to the recipient such a reward should be! For even if knowledge of the true and original Tree of Life, which could have postponed the arrival of old age, is lost, the plants nevertheless remain and renew their flowers, and with gratitude enduring through the years they shall always exhale the sweet memory of your names, and make them more lasting than marble, so that they will outlive those of kings and heroes. For riches vanish, the most stately mansions fall into decay, the most prolific families die out sooner or later: the mightiest states and the most flourishing kingdoms may be overthrown: but the whole of nature must be obliterated before the genera of plants disappear and he be forgotten who held the torch aloft in botany.

The actual choice of words is perhaps not so original; Linnæus never boggled at using the phrases of other authorities when they expressed his own meaning. But they give the conviction that their content is deeply felt and their use instinct with genuine pathos. The superintendent of Clifford's garden proclaimed with the same pride, the same assurance as Horace:

Exegi monumentum ære perennius.

*   *   *

If these pages in *Critica Botanica* give essential information about Carl Linnæus the man, there is another passage in the same book which is of exceptional importance to the understanding of his train of thought. It is the one in which he comments on thesis 271 in *Fundamenta Botanica*: 'All abnormal flowers and plants derive from normal forms.'

It may be questioned whether of all the many experiences in Clifford's garden the most significant for Linnaeus was not the time he spent studying what he called the 'abnormal forms'. Their existence was contrary to the conception of species which was the basis of his *Systema Naturæ*, i.e. that there do not exist any species other than those originally created by God. But in Clifford's garden he saw in front of him each day varieties produced by artificial means. And he could not say that they were merely an optical illusion.

This caused him to cudgel his brains. In *Critica Botanica* he tries in the following way to grapple with the problem. All species derive in the last resort from the Almighty Creator; that is incontrovertible. But the Creator has also permitted nature a kind of sportiveness. 'Therefore there are today two distinct differences between the plants: one a veritable difference, the multiplicity produced by the Almighty's all-wise hand; but the other, variations in the outer shell, the work of nature in a moment of jest.' Of this gardeners know how to take advantage. 'And therefore do I distinguish between the Almighty Creator's species, which are true, and the gardener's abnormal varieties: the former I hold to be of the greater significance for the sake of their Originator; the latter I repudiate because of their originators. The former exist and have existed from the beginning of the world; the latter, which are monstrosities, can only boast a short life.'

It is of no avail that these monstrous forms seem to be the gardeners' idols; if they are neglected 'they glide away and vanish like fleeting shadows'. And Linnæus applies to them one or two lines from the first song of Virgil's *Georgics*:

> Yet is not the success for years assured,
> Though chosen is the seed, and fully cured;
> Unless the peasant, with his annual pain,
> Renews his choice, and culls the largest grain.
> Thus all below, whether by Nature's curse
> Or Fate's decree, degenerate still to worse.[1]

It is easy to understand, however, that this solution in the long run could not satisfy Linnæus. It savours of an emergency exit. Strictly speaking one cannot limit the concept 'to be'. What is 'real' is real, and it is not real in a greater or less degree than anything else.

One corner of the mighty building which Linnæus erected in *Systema Naturæ* began to corrode soon after its completion. Linnæus's cogitation on the abnormal forms in Clifford's garden was the prelude to long mental battles which were to end in the complete abandonment of his original conception of species. In *Critica Botanica* he still seeks to evade the difficulties. But what a rare love of truth, what an outstanding lack of dogmatism is in actual fact evinced by the very awareness and recognition of the problem's existence. Hardly has he completed his system, hardly has he seen it universally accepted and hailed with delight, than he is prepared to question its very foundation. Jealous as he may have been of his work, he was even more so of the truth. And in the history of science and human thought and culture he stands far more alone in this than most people imagine.

[1] Dryden's translation.

LINNÆUS IN EVERYDAY LIFE AT THE AGE OF FORTY
from a drawing by Jean E. Rehn, 1747

CHAPTER VI

PROFESSOR AND ROYAL PHYSICIAN

THE sun accompanied the genius on his way. Home from Holland he practised as a doctor in Stockholm, with dazzling and swiftly won success. He married; the well-known portrait of Linnæus in his wedding garments gives the impression of a man still young; the coat is a gleaming red and behind lowered eyelids one senses twinkling eyes He was made professor, and before long something even more distinguished — royal physician. But he worked hard in Upsala; he worked beyond his strength.

During his years as professor he lectured by turns on medicine (embracing among other things what we today would call sociology), botany, zoology, and geology. He created, as it were left-handed, Swedish geographical and ethnographical research through the accounts of his travels. Every year for more than a decade he wrote Latin works which in different spheres have remained fundamental; dissertations flowed from his pen like leading articles from the journalist of a daily paper, but the majority of them were such that a present-day doctor would have needed ten years to write them. In his leisure hours he transformed the stiff Swedish tongue into a flexible instrument for expressing subtle aesthetic moods. Never in our northern climes has an intellectual fire burnt with such a clear, high flame.

But it was a consuming fire. By the time he was forty Linnæus was tired — not worn out, but ill. *Unjung und nicht mehr ganz gesund.* Dark moods and sombre thoughts prevailed. He was to do much yet. His finest work remained. But he did not smile as he once did.

It is unsatisfactory to try to form a chronology of his inner development. Even during periods of deep depression he could blaze up and give of his best; he wrote *Philosophia*

Botanica when he was mentally and physically tired almost to death. But after entering the forties his temperament ceased to be equable; his cheerfulness and gay defiance disappeared. His sense of great matters, his thoroughness in observing detail and his lyrical enthusiasm grew. But one has the feeling that behind all this there was a nervous tension. He was often peevish. He became rather intolerant. He may have been a swan in a duck-pond, but a swan not only has wings, it has an irritable disposition.

One of the few subjects on which he lectured without at the same time producing any scientifically epoch-making works was mineralogy. He had already made his essential contribution to the systematism of the mineral kingdom. But a collection of listeners' notes from such a series of lectures can be read today by one who has no knowledge of or factual interest in the subject with intense enjoyment, and yet the voice we hear derives from Linnæus when he was least inspired and the listener, in making notes, probably lost the finer shades of meaning and all his characteristic and personal touches.

He has spoken of natural history's justification:

But, Gentlemen, this science brings with it in all conditions its great joy as well as its peerless usefulness, and I protest that everyone should know at least something about it; he especially who is ignorant in this respect will never make much headway with any husbandry. To this end had God introduced into Paradise all the many different kinds, all of whom Adam knew and called by name, each one according to its kind, species, and nature. If we go through all classes, we shall find their peerless usefulness and the indispensable necessity of all in general and each one in particular.
For theology this is as useful and indispensable as any other philosophical science. Clergymen are scattered about the country and will set up house for themselves. It is therefore useful for them to know how they shall arrange all things according to nature's own prompting; among all sciences there is none more valuable, for here are the most objects; I have therefore wished that this should be esteemed the most

important part of philosophy, and be practised and pursued at seats of learning.

It was the generally recognized cultural programme of the age. But behind the programme is the lyrical enthusiasm for 'the most objects', for the diversity of existence. The audience comprised various classes and faculties. The lecture halls were packed. They could be filled even today. The account of the mineral kingdom develops into a great natural epic.

But when the lecturer had finished his explanations and descriptions he grew anxious, as evidenced in a multitude of letters from his pen. If one wants to give a cross-section of his temperament one should limit oneself to a coherent collection. There is one at least, among others, that speaks a distinct language.　　　*　　　*　　　*

After the crisis in Linnæus's life in 1748 one can best follow his changing moods and emotional outbursts in his letters to Abraham Bäck, the distinguished and worthy Stockholm royal physician, in whom he had an implicit trust and who was nearer and dearer to him than anyone else outside his own family. From a purely literary point of view, moreover, it is a most remarkable correspondence. Professor Th. M. Fries writes almost apologetically in the preface to his exemplary edition of the letters that Linnæus evidently 'thought he could not afford to waste much time and trouble writing letters to his most intimate friend', and that 'the letters may very well have been scribbled down hurriedly in his spare moments, *currente calamo*, without making the least pretension to be masterpieces of style.' It is indeed true that both spelling and punctuation are irregular, but otherwise the apologetic tone would seem to be unjustified. In fact I would say that few collected Swedish letters are so well written. If decisive proof be needed that Linnæus was by nature a great writer, among many other things, one cannot do better than refer to his letters to Bäck. In them he often achieves, quite spontaneously, a true greatness of style, and he has the born writer's ability to let this style reflect the facets of his emotional life.

The enthusiasm, the lyricism, the enchanted wonderment that characterize Linnæus's youthful works do not find expression so often in his writings once he has passed the age of forty. But in his letters to Bäck fresh aspects of his personality appear: wit and tenderness, worldly knowledge, irony and humour. He remained changeable, childish, excitable, and suspicious. He continued to make mountains out of molehills. He continued to strike his flag at the slightest setback. But he soon hoisted it again.

Now and then he falls into a purely biblical style. The doctrine of Ecclesiastes concerning the vanity of all worldly things had early taken root in his mind, and it grew stronger with every year he lived. But when such thoughts possess him his writing, consciously or unconsciously, immediately takes on an Old Testament style. He was master of many styles. He had only to choose. And with infallible taste he always instinctively chose the one best suited to his subject.

In October 1748 he writes to Bäck in view of the latter's having failed to obtain the position he had applied for in Stockholm as medical officer of health:

Do not wonder that Strandberg procured the appointment as physician; he had greater merit then my Brother. While Brother ran round in Paris after learning he in Stockholm qualified for many a fine fee. *Fata nostra fatua sunt. Non est volentis, nec currentis, sed miserentis Dei.*[1] God giveth my Brother his bread. Better one hand full in joy, than both full in poverty and lamentation. Brother has already seen the way of the world. The fact that one is fleet of foot does not help in the race, that one is strong does not help in the fight; that one is kind does not help with one's daily bread; that one is wise does not help towards riches; that one is shown grace does not help one properly to understand one's duties.

But all depends on time and fortune. One works to the best of one's ability; more can one not achieve. What does a wise man achieve more than a fool?

[1] The Epistle to the Romans, ix, 16. 'So then it is not of him that willeth, nor of him that runneth, but of God that sheweth mercy.' This text Nils Linnæus once wrote in his son's pedigree, when the latter was visiting Stenbrohult on his way to Holland.

This is no ordinary style of letter-writing. The wisdom now is not only the preacher's, but also sound common sense. The style has also the pith and form of the popular proverb.

Exactly a year later — at the end of October or beginning of November 1749 — Linnæus wrote a letter to Bäck, which was neither finished nor sent, complaining of vexations. He considered himself, as often before, ill used by the authorities; it was otherwise with great men abroad within the realm of natural science, such as Boerhaave and Haller, he contended; they were treated very differently by their countrymen. This theme, becoming quite common as Linnæus got older, now takes the following form:

It is thus becoming more difficult to breathe more, and the bow must be stretched the whole year. What formerly was done with joy, I fear in the future will be done with more compulsion. Should anything befall the Professor, he is thereafter not worth a stiver. Through desire and emulation the nightingales could sing themselves to death, *si Plinio credas*. A mare, whipped daily to make her go, loses her nimbleness. Boerhaave has not been driven to the height he has reached by a flogging each time he absented himself, but by the reward of double remuneration for having been so diligent; and, having received this, he grew all the more diligent, and received treble remuneration. Has not the same happened with Haller in Göttingen?

Grumbling of this kind is the most common thing in the world, among both men and women, but the piling up of fresh and expressive metaphors is peculiar to Linnæus. There is also a breath of poetry in the increasingly common expressions in his later letters of his distaste for life and presentiments of death. 'The stars are hastening towards their setting, one after the other. I am now near the horizon.' Thus he writes in a letter of October 29th, 1765. And one should bear in mind that at that time such language was much more unusual than it is now.

When in 1755 Bäck married a pretty and well-bred girl of but eighteen summers, Linnæus wrote him several heart-felt and joking letters, which also, in keeping with the fashion of the age, were perhaps not over-delicate. Twelve years later Mrs. Bäck died. Linnæus's letter of condolence is remarkable. It begins with one or two warm, simple words, continues with Latin quotations from and Latin paraphrases of Seneca's moral writings, but finishes with the following self-confession:

At a time when I lost a goodly part of my possessions, I consoled myself by thinking that had I, as many others, not had it and received it from our Lord, I should never have mourned. Let my Brother now thank God that in his best years he has owned so agreeable a wife. Remember that only the dregs are left in the goblet of Life; remember that the further down the chariot drives the quicker it goes. Look back on the past life. Is it not like a dream? and such will the future be, if not worse, and at the end anything but a dream. Is one to pity those whose dreams have been shorter; who have escaped the dreary days and many infirmities that old age brings? In truth, none would make a pother about death, if one were not deceived into thinking that one was to live here *in nestereos annos*. In truth, one should count him happy who is overcome by death, which we so greatly fear and believe will be so torturing, for he has thus been relieved of all tribulation.

It is undeniably original as a letter of condolence, especially according to Swedish rules of etiquette; but it is beautifully written. The preceding Latin and its stoic wisdom bear no comparison with this part of the letter written in Swedish.

The temperament reflected in the letters is very unstable, irascible and easily depressed, prone to strong words and expressions. In connection with an academic regulation of which he disapproved he writes (January 29th, 1754):

With us, all the foundations are laid which are promptly to eradicate science; this I have long seen. The principle now is that no one shall be solid, that all shall hasten from the academies merely to gain qualifications; that idiots with qualifications are on a par with a learned man, that *futuri magnates* are idiots who are to give science light.

One must bear in mind that the word 'idiot' was a very strong term to use at that time; now it is used so often in our daily speech that it no longer has such an unkind ring.

Himmelhoch jauchzend, zum Tode betrübt! In February 1758 he writes in a melancholy frame of mind:

I cannot write more today, my tired hand is dropping. I am a child of Misfortune; had I had rope and English courage I should long ago have hanged myself. I fear my wife is again pregnant; I am old, grey, and emaciated, and the house is full of children; who is to feed them?

But the following year, in July 1759, he invites Bäck in the following terms to come and see him (the expression Magnificence alludes to the fact that he was then, for the second time, *Rector Magnificus*, Chancellor of the University):

When my Brother tires of too good living, then come to me as you have promised and stay several days in my kingdom. There shall Brother sit in style to the right of His Magnificence, who is surrounded by his lifeguard of 6 persons and a chief beadle; my secretary daily takes my orders; 2 apparitors, called cursors, are at my beck and call; my army on foot is several thousand plants, and on horseback or on the water more than any potentate's; delegates from the whole world show themselves daily before my eyes in the parade-ground and the auditorium, called the garden. I dispense justice and fear none more than my chancellor. My Brother will find that he is far safer with me amongst all the snakes in the cabinet than among the fairest maids at court. We shall carry out the most vigorous state business amid the monarchy of the plants and politics of the insects, without the smallest adventure.

But it is not only with reference to himself, his own destinies and his own doings that the letters betray wrought-up feelings, intense interest, and rapid pulse. In 1765 an undergraduate, Johannes Wirrwachs, son of an affluent apothecary in Stockholm and a pupil of Linnæus, died and Linnæus writes:

O my God, how dismayed I was today when I heard this sorrowful news. A father and mother lost their only child, their only son; so handsome, so modest and well-behaved; heir to such a splendid apothecary's, so many good things. I counted it as a grace that his father and my dear Brother brought the late little Gentleman to my attention; now I should gladly give a great deal if it had been someone else, for I am heartily distressed. I fear too, that his death will drag his parents to their graves; for what comfort will they have now that they have lost their only and so worthy son. Words and heart fail me, so that I cannot write more.

Even general disasters are mentioned by Linnæus in his letters to Bäck in a way that shows, through the very clearness of the description, how strongly he could feel for others. He describes for instance the great famine in the spring of 1772; the letter is dated March 17th.

It is here prophesied that the coronation will be at Midsummer, but that is too late according to my small calculation. Things here in the country are worse than anyone in Stockholm believes. I fear that I shall not have any under-gardeners this summer to do daily work, for they say they cannot work without food, and for many days they have not tasted a crust of bread. One or two widows here are said not to have had any bread for themselves or their children for 8 days, and are ashamed to beg. Today a wife was sent to the castle for having cut her own child's throat, having had no food to give it, that it might not pine away in hunger and tears. Distress is greater than people think; what will it be by Midsummer; I fear that people by that time will have become desperate; and then anything might happen. I had thought of saving several barrels of barley as seed for my farmers, but people have come to Hammarby from afar, stood the whole day and cried to be allowed to buy barley, so that I could not help letting them have it as long as I had it. I have charged 9 *plåtar* (18 silver dalers); many have offered me another ½ *plåt*; but I have never charged more than 9 *plåtar*, for they have dearly enough paid for it, poor things. If no corn is forthcoming from without, things will go ill. People come with barley, flax, and kitchen vessels, beg people to buy and give them what they wish, for they have nothing to put into their children's mouths.

He has just as good an eye for the comic as well as the tragic side of things. In 1753 he had received a catalogue from a Dutch animal-fancier, called by Linnæus Blåw Jaen. It appears that Bäck, at the instance of King Adolf Fredrik, had asked Linnæus to advise him what exotic animals he should recommend the king to buy. In a letter of July 13th Linnæus answers Bäck in the following words. At the mere thought of the old Dutchman he himself soon falls into a Dutch jargon:

Concerning my good Blåw Jaen, I would rather buy a flask of wine in Holland than animals from him, look twice at mein gield than buy flesh from his shop. He has quite pleasing animals: Eysrere, Ziewet cats, Mier-eaters, etc., but my hair stands on end and the lice bite at the roots when I gaze at the catalogue. 300, 100, 50 guilders; total, a pair of riding horses without a coachman. All the animals are beautiful, but the money is more beautiful. And I begrudge mijn Noble Heer such coa se jelt.
But do by all means recommend the monkeys, for jesting aside there are none so delightful, so strange and different, and for everyone so droll. A *Comedia* may be as amusing as it likes, when the fool comes forward all *spectatores* are given new life; the Creator has made the world a theatre; much had been lacking there, if only a few people and no one else had played Harlequin.

Linnæus's *penchant* for monkeys is familiar to us from his monograph on the marmoset Diana; in this connection it may perhaps be emphasized that the abstract systematist had an unusually concrete eye, a very visual imagination. In a letter of November 30th, 1753, he asks Bäck to consult with a colleague about a Swedish word for the name *amphibia*; it would be agreeable, he writes, to be rid of the Latin in that classification. 'There is no need to make the word *amphibia* Swedish, but merely to get the idea of snakes and frogs, the ugly genus.'
It is a strange destiny that the man who thought and felt so concretely, should be remembered by generations of Swedish schoolchildren chiefly as the discoverer of a multitude of Latin

plant names which they heartily detest and cannot understand.

Linnæus never sought to make himself out better than he was. He seems very candid in his letters. But he makes no bones about informing Bäck in a letter written in Latin in March 1754 that when his private lectures have attracted full houses, this happens *'invitis invidis et ringentibus adversariis'* (to the vexation of those who envy me and the mortification of my enemies). He himself is clearly quite pleased that he is such a thorn in their flesh. He could be touchy, and was not without vanity. But he was alive, alive to an unusual degree, not only in his thoughts, but in his feelings and sensitivity; not a harmonious or a happy person, but one whose lot has consisted 'far too much of marrow and sap, of all life's fiery torments'.

*　　*　　*

A well-known poetic description of Carl Linnæus which is still alive in the consciousness of the people is inclined to make us think of him as gentle and of childlike piety, with a roguish twinkle in his kindly brown eyes, his temperament as bright and clear as a Swedish summer day. But this picture is not entirely true to life. Carl Linnæus was, like other great men of genius, of a complicated and problematical nature. He may well have been a darling of the gods and a Sunday child of fortune in so far as he made scientific discoveries at an early age and early saw them recognized; but not otherwise.

To the traditional picture belongs, amongst other things, the presentment of the Linnean home's unusually harmonious atmosphere. Who has not read poetic descriptions of the magnificent Hammarby, where the august Mrs. Sara Linnæus ruled over a contented people, a bit of a martinet but with a heart of gold and the best imaginable wife for the great scientist who was so inclined to be absent-minded where worldly things were concerned?

The only document, however, which supplies any reliable information about the relationship between Linnæus and his wife, can scarcely be said to confirm these idyllic descriptions. In the middle of the 1760s Linnæus, who by then had become nobleman, knight, royal physician and well-to-do landed proprietor, wrote his will and expressed his last wishes in the following terms:

My freehold estate to go to my widow, so long as she remains unmarried, and after levy of taxes she to give such daughters as are unprovided for a part thereof. But if she contracts another marriage to her misfortune, as I do anticipate, she is to have no part in what I have bought with the money I alone have procured through my labours with books, lectures, and botanizing; but she is then to enjoy her own piece of ground in the town, and according to law a share in all furniture.

If one seeks to form a picture of Linnæus's essentially human characteristics, one must take a document such as this into account. This has not always been done. When this will was drawn up the well-born Mrs. Sara von Linné was a bad-tempered, domineering, avaricious old woman, before whose door it is not reasonable to imagine a long queue of suitors. True enough, there had been evil rumours concerning her; gossip that has been preserved in a multitude of unpublished contemporary notes. There is no need to grub about in or attach any importance to these stories, especially as there is evidence enough that the arrogant, well-to-do wife of an ennobled husband was heartily hated by the professors' wives of the university town. But it must be confessed that the great and world-famous author of this last will and testament, who was tired of honour and renown, had numerous qualities which do not tally with the traditional picture.

In the year 1750 the then forty-three-year-old Linnæus wrote a letter to the secretary of the Royal Academy of Science which is very revealing:

We poor humans, we toil and strive; we make slaves of ourselves, we begrudge our bodies rest at night; and this to acquire merit, to gain grace and favour, to make ourselves skilful, and all we gain in the end is hatred, disfavour, and grief. Of this I have at last seen convincing proof . . . Often have I ventured out upon the sea to bring home gold from Ophir; I have returned with forces so spent, with broken ship and torn sails, and when next I venture out I suppose I shall perish. I have no doubt gained hatred by my diligence; I would wish that I could bring it all to nought. You, Gentlemen, who will outlive me, do not put it down to laziness if you hear nothing more of me, but put it down to the times and destiny. Learn in time to see on what a wretched footing our hope is grounded and how slippery is a patron's favour; now, Gentlemen, you see in another what you may sometime have to taste yourselves.

The reason for the lamentation this time was in the first instance an indisposition from which he had not entirely recovered; to this were added numerous academic vexations. But the letter is by no means unique. Linnæus has very often grumbled and bemoaned his state, regarding himself as a martyr and accusing his fellow mortals and rivals of evil intent and black designs. It is incontrovertible that he had much of the same unfortunately complex nature as Strindberg.

But unlike Strindberg he was no visionary, no emotionalist experimenting with different points of view; his was the most rational and consistent mind that Swedish cultural history has known. He was a scientist. He gave himself unreservedly to his research. He was so entirely absorbed, not only as thinker but also as a man of feeling, in his discoveries — the system of nature, the prevailing conformity to law, the unity which he had found in nature's vast variety — that he grew desperate, tired, nervous, and distracted when everyday life went awry. He was a natural scientist, but a natural scientist whose theoretical passion was related to that of the religious preacher and the poet.

There is a most remarkable letter from Linnæus from the year 1763, when he was fifty-six, and had many times declared that he wanted to bid the world farewell. A certain Captain Ekeberg, employed in the service of the East India Company, had written to Linnæus and offered him a firkin with seeds and plants from the Cape and a living tea-plant. Linnæus answered that such a firkin of things he had always desired but never thought to possess. But a living tea-plant!

But a living tea-plant [he writes.] Is it possible? If it is tea in very truth, I shall make your name, dear Captain, more imperishable than that of Alexander Magnus. But I am sure that they will never reach Upsala unharmed; fate is always against great things. I dare not think of this for perturbation and fear that they may perish on the way. I am old, but were I certain that they were genuine tea-plants, I should venture to Göteborg and myself carry them in my arms to Upsala. If they are real tea-plants, I beg you, dear Sir, for God's sake, for the love of your Native Land, for the sake of natural science, and for everything in the world that is holy and re-nowned, take the tenderest care of them.

It was, this time, tea; it might equally well have been a thistle. Linnæus drew no great distinction. A fact, a botanic, zoological, a moral fact, was to him always the sought-for corner-stone which might make his universal doctrine com-plete.

Linnæus was a poor sinful mortal with all the usual human failings, but a prey to a theoretical passion, a fervent love of the factual, which compelled him to systematize everything — roses, morals, and gastric diseases; which made him tremble with anxiety for the transportation of a plant and coldly note down daily human conflicts.

Such was he. Such he became. His views have in all circumstances been great and far-reaching.

CHAPTER VII

THE PROVINCES OF THE KINGDOM

ON October 17th, 1741, Carl Linnæus took up his duties as professor in medicine at Upsala by giving an inaugural lecture on the subject: 'The Usefulness of Exploratory Expeditions in one's Native Land.' His choice of this particular subject, which had little to do with his teaching, was due to the fact that he had undertaken a journey to Öland and Gotland that summer 'by the order of those in high authority'. Early in the year Parliament had decreed that 'Doctor Linnæus shall this spring make a journey to Gotland, Öland and other places to make himself acquainted with colorific plants and other serviceable plants and herbs'. At the same session of Parliament it was also decided that another year Linnæus was 'to make an investigation in Västergötland as to what *in regno animali, vegetabili et minerali* might there be found of use to the nation'. This expedition, however, was not undertaken until 1746; three years later, 1749, Linnæus set out for Skåne.

Swedish literary historians give Linnæus's accounts of his travels a paramount place in literature, even from a purely aesthetic point of view, but this is perhaps more well-meant than well-informed. It implies an injustice not only towards earlier travellers, Swedish and foreign, but also towards Linnæus himself, inasmuch as it should be apparent to all that in many smaller Latin and Swedish theses he had reached a literary perfection which is lacking in the account of his travels.

The purpose of Linnæus's journeys was also entirely different from that of modern literary expeditions to the same tracts; they were, in the proper meaning of the word, explorations. This must be borne in mind if his style is to be really appreciated. Linnæus wandered through and investigated country that was to a large extent unknown. His pupils went off to Japan and Java, to Africa and South America, to hunt for strange plants and animals and describe the manners and customs of savage and alien peoples, but although their master contented himself with exploring the Swedish provinces, he discovered on his travels in his native land much that was really just as new and remarkable as that which his pupils found in tropical countries. Linnæus, too, found a new land, lighted upon new plants and even animal species hitherto unknown to science, imparted surprising information about the provincial way of living, made notes on the peasants' daily habits and practices which were unfamiliar to the learned, studied an unexplored region and made useful notes concerning industrial and agricultural conditions in various places. They were journeys which it was to the economic interest of the Swedish state to support and which yielded scientific profit. In the introduction to *A Journey in Dalarna* Linnæus says:

Here one can see how much there is at home, and far more besides; see how each province has its own pre-eminence; see how it can be refined; see what unbelievable profit Sweden would obtain if all these provinces were thus thoroughly explored; see how one province can be helped by another's customs.

It is the spirit of the age speaking in these words. Its signature is utilitarianism, paying regard to economically fruitful usefulness. This is not the usual viewpoint for Linnæus to take, for he was a scientist with the scientist's limitations and attitude to life; but it always figures largely in his accounts of any travels, which were undertaken for clearly defined utilitarian ends. The Linnæus who journeyed about the Swedish countryside was not the natural scientist, thinker, and systematist, but the first practical minded observer, who as it were had to show the public that these expeditions, made at its expense, were fully justified.

One would naturally expect the text of these travel notes to be often rather tedious: a long string of descriptions of implements and agricultural methods, fencing, manure and curiosities, cannot be considered as the most captivating kind of reading. Even Linnæus himself has disclaimed all literary ambition:

I have [he writes in the introduction to the *Journey to Öland and Gotland*] presented matters quite briefly, without much argument or many reflections, as they always speak for themselves when the data are correct, and I do this in order that I might gain brevity, which is the most agreeable quality in writing.

But if Linnæus's accounts of his travels are read carefully, it will be found that the thousands of comments unite into a living whole, and eighteenth-century Sweden emerges before the reader's eyes, with its forests and fells, marshes and meadows, and small low wooden houses amongst the trees. It was a Sweden too which by no means lacked its seamy side, and Linnæus acquired with the years an increasingly sharp eye for it.

'For that reason the people are often hungry', he says in one part; and of course this rendered them very susceptible to epidemics. In the far north people did not dare, because of the cold, to have a chimney on the roofs of their cottages, and the smoke caused diseases of the eye, the ravages of which are graphically described by Linnæus. Of the industries in Dalarna he relates:

All those who seek their chief subsistence in the use of the grindstone seldom live to be more than 20, 30 or 40. (From which can be judged the conditions of the widows and dependent children) . . . In church one did see a few grey-haired old men; but it turned out that they were tailors and shoemakers by profession and had not worked in the mines.

Even so, this Swedish countryside, starving and depraved, held a community already heading towards social order and happier living conditions. But Linnæus's eyes were on the lookout for the misery caused by human mismanagement. In Kalmar on May 28th, 1741, he describes a contemporary house of correction:

We saw the other day the slaves or prisoners, who had been sentenced for felonies to labour here at the fortress, being made to haul like horses, and towards evening at 6 o'clock they were driven into dark holes under the ramparts. Four stivers per man were allotted to them each day to live on; when they worked from 6 o'clock in the morning until evening, except between 11 o'clock and 1, they had 2 stivers more, or 6 stivers for their day's toil. Their misery made one's hair stand on end; life was merciless; they were doomed to be prisoners for life.

There were forerunners of the German and the Russian concentration camps.

*   *   *

In Linnæus's later accounts of his travels there is often an elegiac tone, especially in the *Journey to Västergötland* and *Journey to Skåne*. Perhaps it is at its loveliest in a handwritten note which he made in his copy of the *Journey to Skåne*, now preserved by the Linnean Society in London; it concerns his farewell to Stenbrohult on May 16th, 1749:

The evening was calm, Lake Möckeln lay there like a mirror; the lovely beech wood was reflected in the water. The echoes sounded like a sad *vale*, and I said a valediction to the Flora of my youth who had played with me in my childhood days.

But Flora remained faithful to him; she followed him wherever he went and dispelled his heavy thoughts. As he himself writes in one of his letters: 'I have no time to think of illness; Flora comes hastening with all her beautiful companions.' And even in the human kingdom he could find idyllic spots and ways of living that delighted him, and which now, after two hundred years, still delight his readers.

Thus he finds and describes a farm during his journey to Gotland:

Hau was a farm at which we arrived at 8 o'clock in the evening, and I must confess it to have been the most pleasant farm I have seen in the whole kingdom. It had no neighbour for 3 [English] miles around, for on two sides were the sea and a small lake, and on the other two, large and sterile lime flats. It was shared by two farmer-tenants, each having his white and handsome house of stone outside the precincts of the hall, which was built of wood and painted with tar. Inside the houses everything looked clean and decent. The kitchen full of copper vessels, 10 to 15 large and small in each place. The hall was enclosed by hop-gardens and flower gardens, together with large leafy maples, in which had been erected various small wooden cylinders, hollow at the top, so that starlings and other small birds might there lay their eggs and from the leafy trees delight the inmates of the house with constant music.

It is also possible that the womenfolk wrangled and the menfolk tippled at Hau of a winter evening; but to Linnæus, who suffered from melancholy, it appeared perfect. It is also worth noticing how the peasantry of Hau, as early as 1741, interested themselves in nesting-boxes for the birds. It was June 27th when Linnæus decided to spend the night at Hau; and the following day, while continuing his journey on horse-back, he makes especially intimate ornithological observations, among them this:

A bird was heard to give an unusual and violent cry, as though he were in the hawk's claws, but when we looked for him down among the trees we found it to be none other than a little chaffinch with a large white butterfly in its mouth, calling its children home to supper.

It is these sudden and revealing snapshots, if one may use such an anachronism, which for the modern reader lend to Linnæus's accounts of his travels their greatest charm. Occasionally they resemble an English landscape painting; here are a few lines from the *Journey to Öland*:

We set out for Resmo along the escarpment, but below it, having on our left the very steepest part of the escarpment with its bare sides, and on our right the sea. The way lay through the fairest groves one has ever seen, which far surpassed in beauty all places in Sweden and rivalled all in Europe. They consisted of lime, hazel, and oak with a smooth and green soil without stones or moss. Here and there one saw the most delightful meadows and fields. He who has grown tired of this world's inconstant temper and seeks to evade its vanity in a calm *obscuro* could never find a more pleasant retreat.

This could be called literary pre-Romanticism if one were not certain that Linnæus knew nothing of such things; his artistry was unconscious.

Just how dangerous it is to try to apply the somewhat artificial laws of modern literary analysis to Linnæus is evident from an often quoted extract from the preface to the *Journey to Skåne*. Regard should be paid to the circumstances in which this was written. During the winter and spring Linnæus had been afflicted with very nearly pathological dejection, hostility to his fellow creatures, disinclination for work, aversion to life; but the journey to the South-Swedish province, even though it was by no means his favourite part of the country, called forth from him this description, abounding in colour, movement, and sound:

Brown with sorrel are whole fields lying fallow.

Blue of the brightest colour are the sloping fields covered with *Echium*, so that nothing more resplendent can be imagined.

Yellow and brightly gleaming are the fields of *Chrysantemum*, former tilled fields of *Hypericum*, sand-fields of *Stoehas citrina*.

Red as blood are often whole slopes of *Viscaria*.

White as snow are often whole sand-fields of the sweet-smelling *Dianthus*.

Motley are the waysides with *Echium*, *Cichorium*, *Anchusa*, *Malva*.

Everywhere the geese gleam white, fly, snap and shriek in the big fields, so that there is scarcely one old woman hereabouts who does not have geese, there being such a goodly supply of oats.

Swans with their wings raised swim by the shores, mostly at Ellenbogen between Malmö and Skanör, where they are annually shot in large numbers.

The ducks frequent these parts until Christmas time, and even all winter long, unless they are very strong.

Storks, which scarcely venture over Skåne, are seen daily
    walking over the plain on their long legs and building
    their large nests in the villages in trees or on the roofs.
    The rooks caw in all the trees which are planted round
    about the villages on the plain.
The starlings, which together with other migratory birds
    leave the northern provinces after midsummer, sojourn
    down here on the plain and sing in the trees until late in
    the autumn.
The larks hang trilling above all the corn-fields as thick as
    stars, with a daily music.
The nightingales make music every night from the leafy
    groves nearest the plain.
The clock-frogs croak and ring in chorus far into the evening
    without ceasing.

It is superb. And at the sight of all this his frozen spirits
thawed like snow in the sunshine. He was not a harmonious
person; great geniuses very seldom are. But he could never
resist the spring. It is the May wind itself that sweeps through
the more beautiful pages of his travel books.

The mere discovery of a new flower would give rise to clear
and detailed descriptions. He writes in the *Journey to Skåne*:

Sweet-smelling fields between Kristianstad and Åhus, it is
generally said, are to be found in the summertime on the sandy
pastures that lay but a scant 3 [English] miles from Åhus;
people said that this delightful scent is chiefly noticeable at
midsummer, and then more often in the evenings and morn-
ings; they also thought that both rosemary and lavender might
grow here, as in the Spanish fields; and we were curious to see
what it was that delighted the senses. When we came to the
place we found that all this perfume derives from the flowers
of a carnation, which we have never seen further North, but
thereafter met with here in Skåne in all sand-fields and,
curiously, among drifting sand, so generally as to be like a
common weed.

It is the sand carnation, *Dianthus arenarius*, a coloured
photograph of which adorns this book. Linnæus describes it:

DIANTHUS ARENARIUS L. (life size).

SAND CARNATION

Between Kristianstad and Åhus, Linnæus was told by the local people, sweet-smelling sallow was to be found, smelling of both rosemary and lavender at midsummer. 'When we came to the place we found that all this scent derives from the flowers of a carnation, which we have never seen further North, but thereafter met with here in Skåne in all sandfields, and curiously among drifting sand, so generally as to be like a common weed.'

The root of this little Skåne carnation was on the outside a reddish-brown; the many stalks with which it is covered were not longer than a finger, and consisted of two or at most three nodes; the leaves, which are most numerous at the root, were *Clinearia*, and no larger than the needle of a juniper-bush; the flowers were slashed in small fringes, like feathers, white in colour, and occasionally in the middle somewhat grey.

The *Journey to Västergötland* is otherwise the finest, at any rate it has been given the greatest variety and wealth of colour from Linnæus's palette. From the deep woods of Tived with their globe-flowers Linnæus went to Kinnekulle, 'one of the most remarkable places in the kingdom with its peculiar situation and shape'. On the way through Kålland to Skara he saw the wide and fertile plains, 'almost entirely without stone'. In the neighbourhood of Falköping he notes the flower-decked fields. 'The meadows here are everywhere most exceeding fair; but Kleve Heath, with its level fields and many flowers, lay there at this season so charming and fair to behold, that it surpassed all that we have seen of comeliness and splendour the whole summer, indeed, it was so glorious that my pen is altogether impotent to do it justice.'

The region between Borås and Alingsås Linnæus calls the Västgöta Fells, and the forest, he writes, consisted of 'tall and densely growing spruces, so that the sun in certain places could scarcely for a single minute penetrate the dense shadows of the wood'. Approaching Göteborg from Alingsås he is reminded of the Thames Valley, and finally comes to the archipelago with its bare skerries washed smooth by the sea, and 'in the greatest wonderment' Linnæus botanizes at the bottom of the sea as it were in 'a new Sweden'. It is a landscape with a richness and variety entirely its own, and Linnæus could well appreciate it in all its changing moods. This illustrates the falsity of the old but die-hard conception that Linnæus was only capable of appreciating park landscapes and the cultivated plain.

Linnæus has also noted many of the characteristics in the humour of the people. He is apt to linger over the superstitions and strange customs of the country folk, but he also has a good eye for the individuality which is purely human. He relates the most droll stories of the conservatism of the Västergötland peasants, and in Borås he observes that the industrious middle-class merchants did not gladly suffer their sons to attend the academy. One is often driven to reflect when reading Linnæus that provincial outlook has changed less than one would imagine during the last two centuries.

In Alingsås Linnæus is full of admiration for the industrial plants, which he even describes in detail, but he remarks that the air in the textile factories makes the workers delicate. But over Göteborg, 'the fairest town in all the kingdom', shines a cloudless sky. The city, which was then bounded by a kind of moat, appears from Linnæus's description to set the seal on the dawn of a new age. The canals, bordered with trees, remind him of Holland; the façades of the houses give an impression of prosperity; in the streets foreigners are to be encountered and in the harbour lie the East India merchant-men. The head of the East India Company, the great Sahlgren, presented Linnæus with a bird of paradise. The shimmering, exotic creature was a symbol of the incipient prosperity after the poverty of the preceding era, and of the new connections with a strange, wide world.

In the *Journey to Västergötland* there are one or two remarkable descriptions of nature. On his way home through Värmland Linnæus writes on July 30th:

Night drew on with its dense darkness; the owls wailed like phantoms, and the nightjar churred like a spinning-wheel; in the distance Vulcan's pale apprentices thundered and rumbled with more than the strength of their hands, until at 11 o'clock at night we reached Norum after a journey of 1¼ hours.

He had experienced an equally dark night earlier in the trip, on July 8th, at Ingared quite near Göteborg, but the visual impressions then were kinder:

The sky was overcast so that no stars were visible there, but thousands seemed to have fallen to the earth, for tiny lights gleamed on either side of the road amongst the grass; the Creator had bestarred the ground with small glow-worms.

In the *Journey to Västergötland* Linnæus also mentions for the first time *Nemesis Divina*, the grave divinity over whose influence on human life he was to ponder so deeply and so long during the latter part of his life. It was the sight of a poor wretched criminal stretched on the wheel on the road near Brålanda Heath that reminded him of the avenging power that passes through the world. Immediately prior to this he had also been filled with strange broodings. It was in the churchyard at Frändefors. He and his guide had begun reflecting whether one could and should remove the mould from churchyards in order to manure fields and cabbage-patches. Linnæus's argument shows the lengths to which his train of thought could sometimes lead him:

Nature teaches us that we should not consume the corpses of our fathers or our children, and I know not who would have the stomach to do so, unless he were an inhuman cannibal. All nations have made it their business that their dead should rest in their tombs, and that men of honour should be placed with honour in their graves, that they might not serve as food for beasts of prey; the more wealthy have stone and copper coffins made, that their dust may not be scattered abroad; the ancients had themselves and their ashes set in mounds that could not easily be disturbed, and among God's blessings is counted that the bones, body, dust and ashes of the righteous shall rest in peace in their graves; against which, felons of all nations are exposed to worms and wolves, that the ravens shall pick out their eyes, and the bodies of the ungodly God has thrown to the dogs and wild beasts; when plants and animals decay they turn to mould; the mould then serves as food for the plants which have sown themselves and taken root therein, so that the mightiest oak and the foulest nettle are composed through the agency of Nature or a *lapis philosophorum* of exactly the same thing, to wit of particles of the finest humus, which the Creator has placed in each seed in order to change and transform the humus to each its own kind.

Hence it happens that when animals die, they are transformed to mould, the mould to plants, and the plants are eaten by the animals, thus forming the animals' limbs, so that the earth, in the guise of seed, then enters man's body under the name of seed, where it is changed by man's nature into flesh, bones, nerves, etc., and when man after death rots away the force of nature decays and man again becomes earth, from which he is taken.

Thus when plants happen to sow themselves in this mould, they grow luxuriantly, and transform the human earth to their nature, so that the fairest maid's cheek can become the ugliest henbane, and the most stalwart Starkotter's arm the flimsiest pondweed: this is eaten by a stinking Cimex, and becomes such an animal; this Cimex is then eaten by birds and becomes bird, the bird is eaten by man, and thus becomes a part of him. The followers of the ancient philosopher Pythagoras, and to this very day the East Indian *gymnosophistæ*, believed in a *metempsychosin animarum*; we, who hold this as vanity, see another — *metempsychosin corporum*. When I take up mould from the churchyard, I take up those parts which constitute and have been transformed by man into man; if I place this in my cabbage-patch, and set cabbage plants therein, I thereby obtain a cabbage-head instead of a human head, but if I boil these heads and give them to people, they are changed back to human heads or other parts, etc.: Thus do we eat up our dead, and it befits us well; but I confess for my own part, that if I knew that in this manner I were consuming my own or another's grandfather, I were loth to take just that cabbage unless my appetite and hunger were very keen. I well know that nettles grow prolifically in churchyards, where they are diligently gathered by old women, and are bought and eaten in good faith. and that is seemly, though I for my part would rather eat those which had grown in another garden.

Linnæus finishes by saying that one should take good care of churchyards. We should otherwise 'lose our appetite for pork'.

The above has been called the Swedish equivalent of Hamlet's graveyard soliloquy. The theme is indeed the same, but the melancholy which characterizes Hamlet's contemplation of the cycle of matter is entirely absent with Linnæus. He merely states facts; he feels no horror. In the calmest voice he suggests a compromise: since our attitude is what it is, and we feel sick at the thought of eating our forbears, then let us hold the churchyards sacred. But the new channels into which the thought leads arouse in him no perturbation of spirit.

In the *Journey to Skåne* he speaks of the layers of sandstone and slate of which the shore embankment is built up. A gigantic prospect of time opens up before his inner eye. He writes:

I feel dizzy as I stand on these heights gazing down the aeons of time, which have passed away like the waves in the Sound, and left behind them almost worn-out traces of the former world, and which are only capable of whispering now that all else is silent.

But this dizziness was not filled with dread. It was occasioned by aesthetic and theoretical enthusiasm. And it is these wide and infinite prospects that make up the finest reading in the Linnean journeys.

CHAPTER VIII

THE SWEDISH FLORA

T H E divine Flora of mythology was transformed by Linnæus into a text-book over which generation after generation of Swedish children have shed bitter tears. But even so, it can also be said that thanks to this metamorphosis the Swedish plant world became known to our country's inhabitants. No book by Linnæus has meant quite the same to our cultural history as *Flora Svecica*, published in 1745.

For many Swedish children, no doubt, the work with vasculum, press, and herbarium has yielded very little other than the memory of a string of Latin names, which admittedly it does not hurt anyone to know, but which without any link with other interests is a somewhat dry and barren knowledge. When a plant's name has been established, when it has been pressed and pasted into the herbarium with label giving class, order, genus, and species duly attached, many often feel that that is an end to the matter and that they know all there is to know about it. This knowledge is undeniably rather superficial, and there are those who contend that the Linnean plant formalism is to blame for this method.

They would be less critical, however, had they known more of the nature of the botanical excursions which Professor Linnæus arranged in connection with his academic tuition in Upsala. It was certainly not a feeling of dry torpidity that pervaded these outings. One of the participants has thus described them for posterity:

The botanical excursions which he arranged each summer, were just as splendid and entertaining for the young people as useful in stimulating the inclination of the natural historian. They took place in accordance with a certain order defined in a disputation called *Herbationes Upsalienses*, and were arranged to 8 places round about the town. At this time no less than 200 to 300 joined in the excursions and they all set out into the countryside, clad in a white dress of linen, and furnished with all the necessities for the gathering of plants and insects. From his audience he chose some of them for special duties, e.g. one to act as annotator, whose duty it was to note down what he dictated, in case something new occurred; another was monitor, who had charge of the troop's discipline, that nothing disorderly might befall; others were charged to shoot birds; etc., etc.

Everyone gathered at an appointed place, at which he himself was usually among the first to arrive, inducing those who came late to pay a fine. During each excursion certain resting-places were arranged where the scattered students gathered, and where lessons were held on the most noteworthy specimens that they had collected. After the young people had thus from morning till evening thoroughly enjoyed themselves in the countryside, they retraced their steps, their teacher walking at the head and they, in a troop, marching behind him with horn, drums, and banner through the town down to the Botanical House, where a hearty *Vivat Linnæus!* brought the day's pleasures to an end. This joyfulness, enthusiasm, and zest of the young people attracted foreigners no less than local folk to take part in these activities.

In the disputation mentioned, *Herbationes Upsalienses*, Linnæus has briefly told of the purpose and course of these botanical excursions. Usually seven or eight places were visited — Flottsund, Ultuna, Håga, the parish of Danmark, where Hammarby lies, Old Upsala, Vaksala, Husby, and Jumkil. If the destination were Gottsunda they met at Upsala Castle; if they were going to Ultuna they met by the city gates on the Stockholm road. Nowadays these roads are not particularly attractive, but in Linnæus's time they were greener and damper; richer in blossom and bird-song. On the outskirts of the town the professors had their hop-gardens; then came low-lying meadows where the great snipe could be heard in the spring.

An account is also given of the plants which were found on

the way to various places. It is merely a list of names, reminding one of the school tuition in botany of a later age. But there is more to it than that. Linnæus was never content with a mere list of names on those outings. What he used to tell his accompanying flock about the finds is well known from the notes that were made. Several such records are preserved in the university library at Upsala, the Royal Academy of Science, and elsewhere. The best have been published by Fries as an appendix to the second part of his biography.

The professor of course never forgot to give the name of a plant, for that was of the greatest importance. But when a plant had been identified and its place in the system explained, its other qualities were discussed, and the professor would enjoin them to make notes concerning its medicinal use or its beauty or any other peculiarities or traditions associated with it.

Concerning *Lychnis*, he bids them note that it 'is artful in that it lies until it flowers, when it raises itself up, but as soon as the flower has fallen off it lies down again'. How typical of Linnæus to use the word 'artful' in this particular connection! Of the common foxtail it is noted that 'when its seed is put out on a piece of white paper it can be seen to jump around'. This is also an artful observation.

Memoranda on the history of culture, items of medical information, culinary advice, aesthetic verdicts — they all form a delightful miscellany in these herbal records. Of *Daphne mezereum* it is said that 'if the berries are swallowed they cause an intolerable burning of the throat, which is not quenched, but rather increased, by drinking water; a nip of *akvavit* is the best'. A note about *Lathyris*, a kind of vetch, says that the old people called it 'hallelujah' and 'the flower is surpassingly fine'. Of the white water-lily it is noted that the great botanist of ancient times, Theophrastus, said that the water-lily of the Nile, the lotus, sinks down into the water at night. For 2000 years no one noticed that our Swedish white water-lily — not the yellow — has the same idiosyncrasy, until Linnæus drew attention to the fact.

The subjects vary and with them the cadence, and one can almost see the changing play of features in the professor's sunburnt, animated face as he discourses to his pupils. Sometimes it is travel reminiscences. Regarding the well-known *Achillea millefolium* the listening group learns that 'in Dalarna they put it in the ale instead of hops — a whole armful; and when the peasants drink this they become so frenzied that they fly at each other's throats'. And he has this to say about the marsh plant, *Carex vesicaria*:

The Lapps, who experience the very severest cold, and are as good as outside the whole time in their open cone-shaped huts, though they have no stockings can preserve themselves from winter's cruelty by means of this grass, which resists cold and is soft and smooth. The Lapps remove from this sedge the leaves or the grass, dry it and rub it and then place it in their shoes; it gives an incomparable warmth and is quite soft. They also use the grass in this way in the summer that they may not grow footsore, and to take away foot-sweat.

Another time there are glimpses from the world of legend and popular belief. Bracken 'is called by the Catholics "Jesus Christ", for if one cuts off its root there is as it were J.C. Its root cut off obliquely represents a spread eagle.' Of the 'Virgin Mary's Hand' Linnæus relates that the peasants think that if one tuber of this plant is Our Lady's hand, the other is the Devil's; this superstition has arisen from the fact that if the plant is thrown into the water the drier one of the two tubers always floats above the surface, while the other lies below it.

Sometimes there are medical and dietetic prescripts. It is recorded of *Gentiana amarella* that it 'is called by the Germans *surge et ambula* (take up thy bed and walk), since it is excellent for curing the ague and takes away acid from the body. It is used much by peasants against the ague'. And of the black alder, *Rhamnus frangula*, it is said that it 'is excellent as a purgative, when the leaves are dried and the decoction drunk; it never fails, and compares in merit with rhubarb. It should therefore be more generally used'.

Such were the original Linnean excursions. The group round the prophet thinned out by degrees, for everything comes to an end, and the general enthusiasm of the young people for the pleasant science of herbs cooled; the professor grew older; he could not walk so far and his spirits little by little became less gay. It will be seen, however, that it cannot reasonably be maintained that the Linnean method of construing plants was remarkable for dry formalism. It showed a passionate interest for everything closely or remotely connected with the Swedish flora, a taste for curiosities, for living, concrete, picturesque details, a constant variation of subjects and viewpoints, that is characteristic of *Herbationes Upsalienses*. They must have been great fun to take part in.

Occasionally the large crowd would be liberally regaled and entertained by the professor's friends of the surrounding countryside. The sun shone over an Upsala Plain which was green and fragrant and free from dust. The Swedish Flora wakened to the sound of the horn and the drums and the shout of *Vivat Linnæus!*

*   *   *

In a Latin discussion on the sleep of plants, *Somnus Plantarum*, Linnæus writes:

Everyone who has wandered through meadows, woods, gardens or greenhouses on a summer night notices without doubt that everything presents a strange appearance, so that the most skilful botanist has great difficulty in recognizing the most well-known plants that he passes. This change has been generally thought to arise from the variation between light and shadow. We willingly admit that the darkness of night has much to do with it, but a more careful observation has shown that the form of plants at night is usually widely different from their appearance by day, something that has hitherto not been noticed by botanists.

The thesis is a detailed account of different kinds of changes produced within the plant world by the approach of night; it is considered by professional men to be very important. But even in this strictly scientific exposition we sense something of the gentle murmuring of a summer's night. Linnæus was almost incapable of writing of these matters without dwelling on visual impressions from hill and dale in few but descriptive words. He gathered experience in his botanical garden and its green-houses, but to an equal degree in wood and meadow.

His finest presentment of his view on the Swedish Flora, its awakening, budding, blossoming, withering, and death, is shown in the thesis called *Calendarium Floræ*, or the Floral Almanac. It was discussed in March 1756, and is a good instance of the fact that in spite of periods of dejection, and of growing prematurely old, Linnæus's sense of beauty remained just as fresh as it was when the university student presented Olof Celsius with the first-fruits of his brain. Certain parts of *Calendarium Floræ* are full of atmosphere and are among the loveliest things Linnæus ever wrote. That he himself this time was also thinking of something other than the purely factual results is shown by the innumerable quotations from his favourite Latin poets, Ovid and Virgil.

The purpose of the dissertation is 'to give an account of the flowers' successive appearance during the course of the year and the delights afforded us hereby'. Everything has its appointed time, as 'the wisest among mortals', King Solomon, said, and which is confirmed by Virgil: *Stat sua cuique dies.* Ovid's words serve as a motto:

> Autumn brings us fruit, summer flaunts her harvests, spring is decked with flowers. . . .

By establishing the dates of blooming of native plants it would be possible for the farmer and the gardener to decide which duties should be carried out day by day. Such a floral almanac would be a new and better Farmer's Calendar than the old, which 'resting hitherto on a far too slippery foundation, has so fallen into disrepute that it is counted nowadays as ridiculous superstition'.

Linnæus wanted to replace the old months with others, not equally long but measured according to the summer's more or less rapid course. First there is Wintertime, defined thus:

'the egg; colourless; begins.' Then the Thawing of the Frost in the Earth: 'The foetus; white; shows signs of life.' Then come the three months of spring: Sowing Time; 'Childhood Years; pale; develops.' Then the Bursting into Leaf: 'Boyhood Years: green; pushes up stalk.' Finally the Blossom Time: 'the Years of Youth; purple; in flower.'

The summer and autumn months are also three. The summer: 'The Time of Immaturity: the Adolescent Years; red; finishes flowering. Haymaking Time: Young-Manhood years; reddish-yellow; sets fruit. Harvest Time: Full-Manhood Years; yellow; ripens.' The autumnal months are described thus: 'Fruit Time: Years of Maturity; dirty grey; sows itself. The Fall of the Leaf: Old-Manhood Years; grey; withers. Slaughter Time: Years of Decrepitude; brown; wastes away.'

The year's cycle is completed with the Ice Month: 'The Corpse; black; is destroyed.'

Even this scheme is typically Linnean and extraordinarily to the point. On many occasions Linnæus has drawn parallels between the course of man's life and that of the plants. He was, in his natural scientific writings, a strict monist. But the outlook with which in this description of the months he embraces the seasons of the year and both the plants' and mankind's way from the egg — *ab ovo* — to corpse and mould, is unusually wide. One seems to sense the surge of the Heraclitan world flood, and the impression is confirmed by the quotation from Ovid which concludes the account: 'Time passes by unnoticed and cheats us in its flight.'

Linnæus is careful to point out that the information in *Calendarium Floræ* is only applicable to Upsala; each spot has its own calendar. And one wonders if the expectation of spring's arrival in the provinces round Lake Mälaren has ever been more briefly or better depicted than in Linnæus's description of Wintertime and Frost Thaw. Wintertime:

XII: 13. The butter loosens from the churn.

23 The asp's catkins come out.

I: 1. Cracks form in the ice on the lakes.
   2. At night-time the wooden walls creak.
   4. The horse-manure jumps.
   8. Twelfth-Night thaw.
  26. Paul's-Day slush.
II. 22. The iron-days occur, as so often between 20th and 22nd February.

It is still wintertime as the frost in the ground begins to relax its grip, and this transition period lasts from the thawing of the snow until the ice breaks up in the rivers. A quotation from Virgil introduces the description:

While yet the spring is young, while earth unbinds
Her frozen bosom to the western winds;
While mountain snows dissolve against the sun,
And streams, yet new, from precipices run.[1]

And then follows this description of spring:

III: 19. The roofs drip in the noonday sun. The sallow's catkins come out.
    20. The snow thaws by the walls.
        The lark begins his trilling.
    22. The water runs down the walls.
    25. The roads grow dirty and splash.
IV: 1. The horse manure corrodes the ice. The *Lycopodium selago* smokes.
     3. The stones break loose from the ice. 'The hot stone.'
     6. The hills grow bare through the half-thawed snow.
        Snakes creep forth.
        Mosquito swarms dance, flies appear.
        The black grouse is heard.
        The lapwing arrives.
     7. The tortoise-shell butterfly flies about more abundantly.
        The ducks lays her eggs; the mallard arrives.
    10. The melting snow overflows.
        The arrival of the swan and *crex* are sure signs of spring.

[1] *The Georgics*, Book I. Dryden's translation.

The streams rise and the ice disappears.
The pike plays.
11. The water from the melted ice is absorbed into the earth.
Underground cellars become full of water.
The frog appears.

And to finish with, a line from Horace:

Bitter winter is relaxing its grip at the touch of the zephyrs of spring.

Solvitur acris hiems . . . Yes, the words are not out of place. How vague and clumsy most Swedish spring songs seem in comparison with this picture, in which exactness has become poetry. Only one detail seems a little odd: *crex*, the corncrake, does not come until much later; but as I shall show in a subsequent chapter, *crex* must have been written in mistake for *grus*, crane. And this completes the picture. Can one not see the sparkling gleam of Lake Mälaren's April-blue water? And hear the chuckling brooks and the beat of mighty wings? Can one not feel the chill freshness, intoxicating and inciting? Would one change a single detail, add anything or take anything away? In all its brevity is it not perfect?

Thus in the season of Sowing and Bursting into Leaf, Flora comes along with all her companions. It goes without saying that the later descriptions could not have the same graphic clarity; the list of plants is a long one. When the Fall of the Leaf comes, however, and the Ice Month, the descriptions again have the same picturesque strength. But now the words fall dark and heavy, like shovelfuls of earth on the lid of the coffin. It is death approaching.

The Swedish Flora's short life has been painted in this calendar by her greatest lover, so that we sense her fate as though it were our own.

An old German botanist by the name of Hieronymus Bock once wrote, in a herbal book published in 1546, concerning the question of whether the Latin name *Erica* bore any relation to the German heather or not: 'Whether *Erica* be heather or not heather, it is for all that a handsome, noble and merry little bush, possessed of many round, small, brown-coloured twigs, which most decoratively are clad with the tiniest leaves; in appearance like the pleasant-smelling cypress plant.'

A passage like this can of course be said to illustrate how little one knew about the systematism of plants in the sixteenth century, but it also has something to teach even scientific botanists, namely this, that the last word is not said about plants when their systematism has been explained or even when in addition their habitat, chemical composition, and hereditary laws have been analysed. The matter also has an aesthetic side. It has been thought that Linnæus overlooked it. The quotations given in this chapter clearly testify to the contrary. It may very well be that something was lost when the twofold nomenclature created by Linnæus could, thanks to its simplicity and clarity, push aside the picturesque Swedish plant names, which even the learned humanist Olof Rudbeck was not above using in his catalogue to *Hortus Botanicus* in Upsala. But Linnæus found Flora so beautiful that she needed no dress other than the classical, the direct and factual Latin names. Any other adornment did not become her.

CHAPTER IX

THE BIRDS' LIGHT CAVALRY

IN the dissertation *Seneum Salomoneum* Linnæus, in connection with Ecclesiastes, has depicted in very sombre words man's decay and the increasing frailty and decrepitude that come with old age. But through the dark utterances there cuts a single bright ray, not unlike the warbling of a chaffinch on a grey, cold, rainy day.

It says in Ecclesiastes that one 'shall rise up at the voice of the bird'. Linnæus's commentary is to this effect:

In one's childhood and youth one sleeps long and sound. The older we become the more able we are to endure vigils. Boys can be sunk in so deep a sleep that they can scarcely be waked by a box on the ear, but the old man is wakened by the slightest noise. He who wakes during the summertime when the dawn is flushing the sky rejoices to hear the birds with their glorious voices making such harmonious music that nothing can be sweeter. Just as the peasant rises at the crowing of the cock, so does the old man often rise at the first twittering of the birds.

It cannot be said that the passage fits the context. Strictly speaking, consistency should require that the ageing man's defective morning sleep be presented as yet another affliction added to those he already has to bear. In another passage he says: 'How can he who drifts about in the thousand waves of illness and misfortune taste the delights of this life?' One of these thousand waves of misfortune is insomnia. Linnæus should have depicted its horrors. But instead he presents the matter in such a light that a great bliss is vouchsafed the aged. For nothing can be sweeter than bird-song when the dawn is flushing the sky.

It is no exaggeration to assert that whoever could be guilty of such inconsistency in a medical thesis must have had a very strong feeling for the beauty of bird-song. He must have been of the opinion that listening to it outweighed many annoyances and that it has the power to dispel the apprehension of ill-health and the thought of death's threatening approach. It is an unmistakable autobiographical confession.

It is not the only time Linnæus testifies to his love of birds. In *Systema Naturæ* he calls them *æreæ vocales volucres pulcherrimæ*. It was the winged and musical beauty, the colour that he loved. He knew them well too. Admittedly, it is easy to find ornithological mistakes in his books, particularly in his youthful writings; in the *Journey to Lappland* he takes the black stork for a heron; in the *Journey to Dalarna* he confuses grebe and diver. But this is due to obscurity in terminology and classification, not to defective observance. One must mind what one is about when tackling the problem of correcting his ornithological statements. Thus Th. M. Fries, who was not only the foremost but also the most reverent authority on Linnæus's writings, has made quite needless marginal notes when he translated the charming thesis, *Calendarium Floræ*. Linnæus states that on May 9th the swallow and the stork arrive. Fries remarks that since the stork is not found near Upsala he has translated the word as crane and not stork; this with all the better conscience as crane should have been mentioned somewhere in the work. What Fries forgets is that the crane does *not* come to Upsala on May 9th together with the swallow, but a good month earlier; Linnæus has assuredly meant what he wrote, but the stork he had in mind was not the white one, which he had never seen north of Skåne, but the black one, whose existence Fries has clearly forgotten. Against this, Linnæus has noted for April 10th that the swan and *crex* are sure signs of spring; Fries remarks rightly that *crex*, the corncrake, occurs later. But in the original Latin manuscript Linnæus had no doubt written *grus*, crane, and not *crex*; easy for a printer to confuse, easy too for Linnæus to overlook.

It must be admitted in all fairness that whoever reads the avian classifications in the later editions of *Systema Naturæ* or in *Fauna Suecica*, is not likely to get a very strong impression of Linnæus's intense love of the world of winged creatures. As has been pointed out in an earlier chapter, the strength of the ornithological systematism which Linnæus introduced lay in the fact that determination of classes and species was concentrated round definitions of beak and claw. It cannot be denied, however, that a Scandinavian tradition has grown up which has called itself Linnean, whose biased interest for beak and claw has, not without reason, been made the object of ridicule.

It is by no means only the beak Linnæus deals with in the lectures on the animal kingdom which he began in 1748 and continued in the spring term of 1751 and 1752. Of the nightingale he says that it sings best of all birds, and 'can move one's inmost being when of a summer evening one listens to its pleasant song'. It is the aesthete's view of the subject. And when he speaks of the goldfinch he lingers in detail over its merits as a cage-bird and how it should rightly be treated in captivity. The cultural-historical element in these animal monographs is often large. Whatever is concrete, observed, and personally experienced has a prominent place. Often Linnæus dwells on what he has seen with his own eyes during his travels in the Swedish provinces. One of the birds which has been dealt with in greatest detail — as far as one can judge from the listeners' notes — is the black grouse. There is practically no mention of the black grouse's bodily structure, but a great deal is said about its call and habits, about different kinds of grouse hunting and methods for taming the birds. 'To have black grouse tamed in the house is very artful', Linnæus contends.

He can even speak charmingly of the reptile family, which he so greatly disliked, with numerous details of curious facts. He says of the slow-worm:

The old peasant women firmly believe that the cows will thrive if they first rub their hand on the slow-worm and then rub the cows with their hand, but what makes the cow thrive is not the slow-worm but solely the rubbing itself, which makes a slight tickling in the skin, and this motion, however slight, is nevertheless most beneficial.

These are memories from the farm at Stenbrohult, where the dairymaids had a deep-rooted belief in the sacredness of snakes and a veneration for their portents.

Where the unknown is concerned, the exotic animals, his joy in the fantastic, and his love of the fabulous sometimes get the better of his critical judgment. What old Herodotus relates in his History about the crocodile pales beside what Linnæus has to tell his students about this Leviathan. He informs them, *inter alia*, that those who are accustomed to the crocodile 'can throw themselves on his back, bridle and ride him like a horse'. The sight that Linnæus has seen in his imagination — a horde of Egyptians galloping along the banks of the Nile on frisky crocodiles — has evidently amused him so much that he hates to banish the picture by examining its plausibility.

*   *   *

Linnæus shows how practically familiar he was with the Swedish bird world in the thesis published in 1757 on the migration of birds, *Migrationes Avium*. The introduction is one of his finest tributes to this family so dear to his heart:

To the many good things with which the Almighty Creator has endowed man on this earth, for his use as well as for his joy, belongs the gift of birds. These have greatly appealed to my sense of beauty, and their appearance is so lovely that to my way of thinking there is nothing which contributes in a greater degree to the pleasure of the human race. What can compete with the humming-bird's dazzling beauty? What can surpass in splendour the peacock's colourful tail? These are, however, not nature's only works of art deserving our attention: every bird, if we regard it with due care, presents a rich subject for admiration. We shall see them all gleam with the changing play of colours, which follow each other in the most ingenious succession and mutual rivalry— I doubt if the most skilful painter can so mix his colours as fully to reproduce nature in this respect.

If we regard birds' feathers and their peerless structure we shall clearly see that there is not a single feather which is not assembled by the great Artist with such skill that the whole of our short life span is insufficient to explore and rightly explain its mechanism and to muse upon His wisdom.

The problem he has selected for discussion in the thesis is one of the most difficult in ornithology, i.e. migration, and is still today by no means completely solved; in spite of several perspicacious foreign observers it was not until ring marking was used that there were any definite facts to go by. How great the uncertainty was when Linnæus intervened can best be seen from the confused speculations of the learned. One example will suffice.

In 1718 a book appeared in London: *Philosophical Letters between the Learned Mr. Ray and Several of his Ingenious Correspondents*. It is a work of the greatest value; the great Ray, or Rajus, whom Linnaeus himself set great store by and from whom he had learnt much, here discusses with other scientists a number of important questions. One of his correspondents by the name of Johnson writes to him on one occasion as follows:

While I think of it, I beg you to advise me, when occasion offers, whether you can say anything definite concerning migratory birds, whither they go and when they leave us? Even if it is admitted that the swallow family and similar small birds conceal themselves in rock crevices or in trees, yet storks, geese, and other large birds cannot very well do this. To the moon the journey is far too long, and the temperate zone in the New World I scarcely think they could reach, having regard to the fact that wild geese from Ireland and woodcock from Norway are often so fatigued when they reach us: and moreover it seems to me no less difficult a problem to explain how they can avoid being seen by so many alert observers, both on land and at sea, especially since maritime commerce has increased so much amongst us.

Knowledge of the subject had not progressed much further than Aristotle when the eighteenth century was young.

Fredrik II of Hohenstaufen, the great medieval emperor, knew more about the migration of birds, but his large and comprehensive work on falconry was by this time long since forgotten.

But Linnæus's thesis *Migrationes Avium* is up to date to a surprising degree. His literary works of reference were not many; he has used a German and an American ornithologist's observances and drawn conclusions from what his own pupil Hasselqvist told him in his letters from Egypt; in the main he has had to rely on his own observations and judgment. Nevertheless, his account of the Swedish birds' migration is for the most part correct, and rich in detail showing the sharpness of his eye. The most remarkable thing of all is surely the fact that long before anyone else he seems to have found out about their three great highways across the Mediterranean. He knows which birds do and do not migrate, often when, not seldom whither, and sometimes even how they migrate. Such a knowledge meant lengthy and accurate studies out in the woods and fields. Linnæus writes in the preface: 'I went into the woods and the peaceful groves, whither these winged creatures take refuge, examined them carefully and impressed my observations on my mind.'

It was living knowledge he acquired.

*　　*　　*

He still speaks with manifest tenderness of *aves*, the birds, in *Deliciæ Naturæ*, his valedictory speech on relinquishing the chancellorship in 1772: 'Cavalry, light, nimble, resplendently clad.' The amphibians, on the other hand, are mentioned thus: 'an ugly, horrible, naked pack, on foot.'

We have already seen how, on his journeys through the provinces of the kingdom, he speaks in a special voice of the birds. But the best of the bird descriptions from his travels has been saved for this chapter. It is the brilliant painting of the skua in the *Journey to Västergötland*:

Elof was the name of the blackish gull here which cannot itself dive into the sea to catch fish, but is created a robber among the gulls. One saw with amusement how this

Cossack pursued the other gulls the moment they had caught a fish, and continued to pursue them until they had to disgorge the fish they had caught and already half swallowed. I have watched with wonderment a tame gull I had in the Academy Garden, and saw that, however little food he may have had, if anyone chased him, he soon disgorged what he has eaten. This power of easily vomiting, the Creator has used to support our Elof family. The gulls often fish more than they should, and can well afford to give some of their treasure to Black Bob. But against this, Nature has so arranged it that this skua may not increase too much, so that he is also the rarest of all gulls. It may be added that this ne'er-do-well hunter is not over delicate; for sometimes the gulls when they have eaten nothing, open the back door when chased and cast him tainted food, to which Elof also helps himself. Black Bob is very agile, and always catches the food in the air when it is thrown to him. Nor is he shy, for when the fishermen see him and call 'Elof, Elof', showing him a little fish in upstretched hand, Elof comes flying towards the boat and catches the fish as soon as it is thrown. Elof always keeps to the most frequented parts, and prefers to stay by fishing hamlets, where there is a wedding every day with games and dancing. The Ångermanland man does not like to see him shot, for by his presence he shows the whereabouts of the herring shoals.

As a depicter of animals Linnæus has otherwise achieved his best in the series of monographs published in the papers of the Royal Academy of Science. There are perhaps not so many descriptions of birds, although these are excellent: the Indian sparrow, the golden oriole, the fulmar, and several others. Even in these technical descriptions he liked to include such traits as seemed to him wonderful and which appealed to him, so strongly susceptible was he to all that is mysterious in nature, in the prescribed order of the universe. He concludes his monograph on the fulmar thus:

This bird has an admirable quality which we should not pass by unnoticed, but rather praise the all-wise Creator's incomparable arrangement whereby, through this bird, mariners tossed on the surging ocean may know quite 6 to 12 hours in advance when a severe storm is approaching, and be prepared for it by taking in sails and taking other necessary precautions. The bird senses in advance when a storm is on the way, seeks out the ships and keeps constantly by them, so that he may shelter on the lee-side of the ship when the storm comes, for otherwise he would be fatigued to death by the violence of the waves. As soon as mariners notice the birds' presence they can be certain of a storm's being on the way.

It was another insight into the plan of creation which the study of the fulmar gave to Linnæus.

But the most remarkable Linnean animal monographs in the papers of the Royal Academy of Science are those that deal with mammals: with the lemmings — 'Observations on the animals which are said to come down out of the clouds in Norway' — ; of the racoon — 'Description of an American animal ' — ; of the marmoset, 'Diana'.

His explanation of the popular belief that the lemmings come down from the clouds is superb:

When the Lapp sees on the horizon a small, dark speck of cloud he knows that if he is in a pleasant place he should stay there, or otherwise hasten whither he can encamp himself comfortably. The cloud comes up by degrees higher and higher and grows steadily bigger and bigger, finally occupying half the heavens, and bringing with it a strong wind, and finally in the form of a dense fog encompasses both man and beast; the wet particles cling to every hair; it becomes so dark that one can with difficulty see one's hands, seldom one's feet, and then suddenly, all grows quiet, there is no wind, and yet, when one calls, he cannot be heard even at a distance of 9 ells. If one walks in this mist, when one cannot see the snow on the ground, it is easy to stumble into a crack made by the water and be buried there; whence comes the saying that the clouds make away with Lapp and reindeer and cast them down the mountain-side. But the cloud is no more able to lift anyone than a mist; that is, not even these mice, which breed and are born like other animals in the mountains, and swarm therefrom in certain years, as it were in colonies. In former times, when these animals suddenly covered the whole countryside in those provinces lying adjacent to Lappland, the people grew dismayed, for it was a sight they never before had seen, and they imagined that it was a punishment called down on them by God for not having kept their days of prayer. This had once happened in the parish of Lima, the priest there told me.

The destitution and hazards of the wilderness are movingly portrayed by Linnæus, who not only could explain popular beliefs but also had a sympathetic understanding of them, so that even when he solves a seeming miracle his wonder still remains. His description of the lemming procession towards death and distant seas is filled with mysticism.

He has also written concerning his study of the racoon and the marmoset Diana. In both cases he is concerned with wild animals which he has had with him at home, played with, studied and grown fond of as individuals and friends. Among later authors I know none other than Brehm who has been able to write of captive or tamed animals, so concisely but yet with exhaustive characterization, so warmly but at the same time so factually and unsentimentally. And in the midst of his delight in the racoon's comical idiosyncrasies Linnæus observes that what most aroused his wonder concerning this favourite in his home was the structure of its reproductory organs. In his characteristic way, Linnæus reflects deeply on the Creator's meaning in this respect.

Lively appreciation of the marvels of creation is the Alpha and Omega of the Linnean zoology. In 1740 he wrote a paper for the Royal Academy of Science with the title 'Thoughts on the Basis of Economy through Nature-Study and Physics'. The paper is designed to show how a country's finances can be advanced by the spreading of knowledge of nature's three kingdoms. The purpose is thus utilitarian. But Linnæus was so made that he could never limit himself to the purely useful aspect. In dealing with the economic advantages to be gained by man from the animal kingdom, he suddenly exclaims:

What can be compared with the size of the elephant, the fleetness of the horse, the strength of the aurochs, the cruelty of the tiger, the splendour of the peacock, the jaws of the shark, the mouth of the crocodile, the poison *cobræ de capello*, the song of the nightingale, the delight *remoræ*. One sees the animals running on the ground, the birds twittering in the air, the fish gleaming in the water, the insects flashing everywhere, and all in their own way gratifying and serving us.

To this one might object that it is not exactly easy to determine in what way the tiger with his cruelty and the shark with his jaws gratify and serve us. In point of fact Linnæus has added the last words merely because the purpose of the paper and the preceding train of thought so demanded; he discovered suddenly that he had got carried away. For as far as he himself was concerned the crocodile's mouth did arouse his wonder, his enthusiasm, his deep piety.

'Upon earth there is not his like, who is made without fear' as it says in the Book of Job about Leviathan. Linnæus saw most animals with such eyes. He found each one more wonderful than the other. The shark's jaws aroused in him the desire to praise and laud the Creator.

    *   *   *

The eighteenth century had three outstanding natural scientists, born in the same year — 1707 — to a certain extent alike in that they were great, meditative, mystical, almost omniscient: Linnæus, Haller, and Buffon. They never liked each other. Their paths, too, lay apart. Buffon could never conceal his contempt for the Linnean natural system; to his way of thinking, there was no prescribed order; one must accept reality as it was, without order and contradictory, and describe creation case for case. This he did in *Histoire Naturelle*, which deals with the universe in its entirety, with the earth's history and its character, with man as a social entity and biological phenomenon, with all the animals. He had considerable help in its composition; he was an aristocrat with eminent position and large income, but probably most of the actual writing he did himself.

The result is something quite unique. In a grandiose style

reminiscent of the seventeenth-century French preachers, he has painted the destinies of the earth and its inhabitants; the final impression is very melancholy; like Linnœus, he has attached chief importance in the Bible to the mournful wisdom of Ecclesiastes. He contended that man must be unhappy to the extent that he was afflicted with a soul, and in the animal world he sensed the sigh of the beasts. In his distinguished status— he was Director of the Jardin du Roi, Member of Academy of Sciences and a Fellow of the Royal Society, London— he would work from dawn to dusk and his methods were as follows: when he was about to begin with a new animal species in his *Histoire Naturelle* he got his numerous amanuenses to collect everything that had previously been written about it and to inquire for any new information from the French provinces; he would then adapt the material to his general view of life and write down his monograph. There is nothing to indicate that he himself had any desire to see with his own eyes the animal he was describing.

But what he achieved was, even so, magnificent. Swedish literary historians are accustomed to write, after French prototypes, that Buffon could really only describe such animals as the lion, which had great heraldic significance, or the horse, which was the servant of human culture. This is an unfair verdict, for on the contrary, Buffon was at his best in his descriptions of birds. It can be said that neither before nor after him has there been a writer who could equal him in describing in detail the beauty of birds or the sweetness of their song.

A question which French literary historians have still by no means solved is what share Buffon's amanuenses had in the composition of the many grandiose tirades that occur in his works. But the mixture of quiet observance of detail and restrained passion peculiar to Buffon is clearly apparent in his writings. In comparison with his description of the nightingale's song Linnæus's apostrophizing is inexact, rhetorically expressed and listened to sensuously. But it may also be that Linnæus enjoyed the music in a more objective way than

Buffon. It is really the difference between those who, like Buffon, are absorbed in details, who try to extract all values from them and make these the expression of their own philosophy and sentient life, and those who, like Linnæus, are systematists, who for that matter never forget the main issue, and who cannot listen to a nightingale without at the same time musing on the aesthetic harmony of existence.

The ecstatic mood in the face of concrete natural experiences which inevitably finds biblical expression can be noticed, on the other hand, in a German writer, who in his native land, and even in Scandinavia, did more than anyone else during the nineteenth century to spread knowledge and love of the animal world, namely, A. E. Brehm. By disposition Brehm was a rationalist; he was in sympathy with the contemporary doctrine of evolution, and adopted a clearly inimical attitude towards the Christian faith. Nevertheless, he snatches in the same way as does Linnæus at religious terms (in his case, too, reminiscences from a happy childhood in a Protestant vicarage) when he wants to explain some overwhelming impression he has received during his expeditions into the wilds. His colouring is often more vivid than Linnæus's (especially in his discourse on the African jungle in his book *From the North Pole to the Equator*), but the transition from, for example, the croaking of the frogs in the swamp to a choir of angels exalting God's works, testifies to a way of seeing and feeling which Carl Linnæus introduced. It can be summarized in Goethe's words:

> Die unbegreiflich hohen Werke
> sind herrlich wie am ersten Tag.

After Buffon the greatest of the eighteenth-century writers on birds was Audubon, also a Frenchman, but only by birth, as he lived most of his life in America, where his name is just as living and topical as Linnæus's is with us. This young Frenchman was a passionate nature worshipper, a great artist and an exceptional stylist. The result of his walks and excursions into the woods was the production of the most superb bird pictures which have ever been executed, and a series of mighty volumes, incredibly expensive, which he managed to place all over the world, especially in England, where there were many wealthy men with a love of nature and beautiful books.

When one gazes now at Audubon's pictures and reads his text, one is immediately struck by the gulf between him and Buffon. Audubon is a hunter and a collector, an explorer, with not much philosophy, but whose eye lights up every time he sees a bird. He had read and learnt from Buffon. He would probably have written and painted as he did in any case, but when he dared to think that his work also had a scientific importance, it was because Buffon was not his only household god. He also worshipped Linnæus. And in his style and his outlook he follows in the Swede's footsteps.

In Sweden the specifically Linnean manner of describing animals has not influenced our relevant literature to the degree one would have expected. The Swedish writers on animals who are Linnean in style and outlook have been neither numerous nor exceptionally good. There are, however, one or two, and among them is Carl Clerck. When, in 1757, he published his classic work on the Swedish spiders, *Aranei Svecici* — still the standard work on the subject — Linnæus was particularly enthusiastic, as appears from his correspondence on the subject. In this lovely book, whose pictures are an abiding source of joy, there is in the manner of observation and in the turn of phrase a nuance that is purely Linnean. This is how Clerck describes the spiders' wedding (*Pars prior*, § 9):

The males and females do not normally consort together; but with the greatest fear and cautiousness approach each other to satisfy the desire they mutually feel for the propagation of the species; they do not remain especially long together at one time in their love overtures before they hastily separate, as it were in alarm; but they soon recommence the same game, several journeys over again, but with decreasing ceremony and evasion. Finally, after conception has been accomplished, they hurry away from each other in the greatest haste.

This is the Linnean sense of the 'artful' and the curious; the regarding of things with an amused raising of the eyebrow; the succinct method of description originally deriving from Aristotle; and, from a literary point of view, very charming.

English literature's classical eighteenth-century author in this field was Gilbert White. He was a Linnean. If one looks at the matter from a literary rather than a scientific point of view, it can be safely stated that the Linnean observance of nature won a greater following in England than in Sweden. After Linnæus's death we took no further interest in the realistic and at once artistic portrayal of nature; for our great romantic poets nature was a symbol, a reflex of human moods and state of mind. If we look at contemporary Englishmen we notice the difference. With many of the English romantics — both poets and prose-writers — we meet nature not only as dream and thought but also as clear and sound reality, and English literary historians have observed that this is no doubt partly because Gilbert White's book on Selborne has been so generally read and loved. It was quite near Selborne, in Winchester, during solitary autumn walks on Gilbert White's territory, that Keats wrote his 'Ode to Autumn'. And through White's agency these wonderful stanzas have a remote connection with the first rambles at Stenbrohult of the Swedish clergyman's son.

Gilbert White once wrote that he had at last discovered the clearest sign of God's wisdom and power. It was in the bodily structure and colouring of the black-throated diver. And this is more Linnean than Linnæus himself.

In Rasleigh Holt-White's great work *The Life and Letters of Gilbert White of Selborne*, one gets a strong impression of the enormous weight that the name of Linnæus carried in cultured circles in England during the eighteenth century. The greatest distinction an Englishman — whether an amateur or academically qualified — could dream of at that time was to be mentioned in one of Linnæus's works, and to that end they sent him innumerable suggestions for the alteration of the classification of species in *Systema Naturæ*. When Gilbert White's scientifically educated brother John pointed out to Linnæus that he had classified a variety of the whinchat family as belonging to the swallow genus, he was in a state of excited anticipation for years, waiting to see if a new edition of *Systema Naturæ* would mention his name. Veneration of the master was very great; people refused to the very last to believe the rumour that Linnæus's mental powers were beginning to fail with age; and when Sir Joseph Banks received a very harsh letter from Linnæus to the effect that the collections from the Banksian South Sea Islands expedition which he had presented to Upsala were not sufficiently large, the rich English voyager grew anxious and distressed, but it would never have occurred to him that Linnæus's self-assumed demands were not fully justified. Linnæus could make mistakes in zoology, as both Pennant and the White brothers admitted, but those who cavilled at the oracle of Upsala were, in their eyes, like 'the infidels who rage at the saints, though at the same time they must feel themselves edified by them'.

To give precise details of Linnæus's importance in Gilbert White's Selborne book is superfluous; it is evident on every page. A more risky task is to fix the definitely Linnean style in later English natural history writing. In the first place, English literature's general development is to a large extent dependent on the view of life and nature which the English natural historians have possessed. Secondly, one can indicate at least one or two points in the literary development where the Linnean element is obvious. The man who introduced into English literature the concise, popular and, as far as the noting down of species was concerned, complete art of describing animals, which was based on literary studies and personal observation, was Thomas Bewick. In his *General History of Quadrupeds* and even more so in his *History of British Birds*, wonderful books from the beginning of the nineteenth century, all the concise monographs have something of the Linnean descriptive style; apart from the purely factual (information concerning coat or plumage, frequency or propagation), there is often a passage of purely aesthetic or emotional content; the atmosphere of the woods, the joy of grove and meadow, a sudden visual impression, they are all recorded. This mode of expression has become so normal that even at the present day an author such as J. Lewis Bonhote, in the much used standard work, *Birds of Britain*, completely follows Thomas Bewick's pattern.

Darwin cherished intense admiration for Linnæus. This was possibly, in the main, because of the latter's purely scientific achievements, but the method of representation in Darwin's book, *Formation of Vegetable Mould through the Action of Worms*, has the Linnean feeling of joy and love of what is quaint. Ornithologists such as the great humanist Warde Fowler and the writer W. H. Hudson follow the same line.

Last but not least, this tradition is evinced in England by Viscount Grey. Its import is clearly apparent in one part of his book, *The Charm of Birds*. The author is talking of a Christmas morning at Fallodon. As the sun rose over the pond the birds became for a moment almost wild with joy, they chirruped and sang, flew backwards and forwards, splashed about, dived and shook their wings. Grey watched them from a garden-seat until calm reigned once more. The sun continued to shine on the water, the birds' plumage, and the cold, bare branches of the trees.

Anyone who had come upon it now might have thought that the place was under some spell. He would have seen the man on the seat sit motionless, too, for a long time; entranced rather than asleep; the scene had indeed sunk down into his heart and 'held it like a dream'. There are times when man's consciousness seems laid to rest in some great whole, of which he has become a part. There are hours of which it can be said, 'Thought was not: in enjoyment it expired.' So it was now, and if anything stirred in the mind at all, it was an echo of the words, 'And God saw that it was good.'

When these lovely words were written, it is improbable that Lord Grey was thinking of Carl Linnæus. But even so he was, in one way, fulfilling a Linnean tradition, and it may well be that its quintessence has never been more intelligibly and appositely expressed.

CHAPTER X

PHILOSOPHIA HUMANA

DURING the terms 1742-43, 1748-49, 1752-53, 1755-56, 1759-60, 1763-64, 1767-68, and 1771-72 Linnæus lectured publicly on dietetics. These lectures were extremely popular; there were usually a couple of hundred students present in the lecture hall; in all probability neither before nor since has a professor at a Swedish university attracted so large an audience. It should be noted that of this audience scarcely more than half are likely to have been medical students; the remainder gathered in the hall out of sheer interest in the subject and the lecturer. One of Linnæus's earlier biographers has testified to this from his own experience: 'When speaking of the precepts of diet, he often made his pupils roar with laughter at the picture he drew of the absurd fancies then in vogue, and with a light and pleasant jest he would impart the most useful knowledge concerning the care and preservation of one's health.'

Dietetics were a comprehensive subject in the Linnean curriculum. They really signified not only diet but also ethics. The lecturer had first and foremost to investigate which foodstuffs and daily habits could be considered suitable for health. But this immediately brought him to the question of what was essential and inessential in life, beneficial or injurious. The medical remedies and experiments were the outline of a philosophy of life. It was the great Paracelsus who introduced this study, and there is little doubt that Linnæus, directly or indirectly in many instances, was a disciple of Paracelsus. The doctor was a philosopher.

Fortunately we can form quite a good conception of what Linnæus taught from the rostrum when giving his lectures on dietetics. There is an original manuscript in existence which Linnæus, in his mythological language, has called after one of the Fates, *Lachesis Naturalis*. It is composed in Latin, with a mass of Swedish words and phrases interspersed, evidently used for the simple reason that at the moment of writing they seemed to Linnæus more expressive than the Latin. This manuscript may be regarded as a rough draft or a résumé of the lectures on dietetics; perhaps it was a mnemonic list for use during the lectures; perhaps it is the first sketch of a planned presentment of the subject in book form. We cannot be sure. There are, furthermore, a number of notes taken down during the lectures by Linnæus's pupils over a period.

The Lachesis manuscript is furnished by Linnæus with a sub-title: *Philosophia Humana*. This title is fully justified. It really is a human philosophy which Linnæus puts forward in his lectures on dietetics. To be sure, they deal to a large extent with food and drink, apparel and bodily movement, but they also touch on the ultimate objects of life, on the questions of happiness, death, and of God. The Linnean way of thinking is nowhere else so clear and well defined.

The work can be regarded and valued from different aspects. A writer on the history of culture could hardly find a book which gives a more intimate picture of contemporary Swedish everyday life. As a contribution to the history of medical practice in Sweden it is without equal in our eighteenth-century literature. But even if we limit ourselves to the biographical aspect and are content with trying to determine what it tells us about Linnæus's thoughts and personality, we must bridle our desire for quotations. In an extremely pithy manner Linnæus here discusses the highest and lowest in human life, and both when he speaks of eternity and when he speaks of sense-perception, one seems to be aware of the personal accent, the living sound of his voice.

If one is to give an indication of the contents of the work, one should not differentiate between the Lachesis manuscript and the notes made at the lectures; the thoughts and the plan of presentation are in both cases the same. Perhaps it should also be premised that the reader must accept the Linnean thesis that *naturalia non sunt turpia*. Linnæus unites in his dietetics the peasant's drastic and frank imagery with the Spinozistic philosopher's conviction that everything that happens is a necessary process of nature, raised above human valuation.

Linnæus is to lecture on health, on the concept *Sanitas*. He quotes by way of introduction a number of more or less august, biblical, classical, and modern authorities, but the subject of health is soon abandoned and Linnæus passes on to the subject of *mors*. Death is the most terrible of all: *Mors est omnium terribilium terribilissimum*. But Linnæus, who once did not and soon will not exist, wants, in terms reminiscent of the Koran's adherents, to praise the Living One who never dies: *Deum omniscitum omnipotentem, ut in sua majestate viderem, huc accessi, qui nec fui, nec ero*. Happy are we in that we can forget our fate, although, he hastens to add, none is completely happy before death: *Ante obitum nemo beatus*. And he quotes from the second book of Chronicles:

Behold, I will gather thee to thy fathers, and thou shalt be gathered to thy grave in peace, neither shall thine eyes see all the evil that I will bring upon this place, and upon the inhabitants of the same.

He adds that by nature we are not only unhappy but also evil. He cites St. Paul:

For the good that I would I do not; but the evil which I would not, that I do.

With that certainty it is easier to accept the frailty of our life-thread.

He has, however, a word of solace; but it does not concern a life after this one, it concerns the sensations of agony at the moment of death. He relates:

It is said in an old proverb: Toil as one will, the worst yet remains, namely death; it seems to be so, and there are few who have come back from death and can tell us anything of this. In the war between Holland and the French, the French captured a Dutchman, whom they hanged from a tree; 3 hours afterwards the Dutch came along and cut him down, blew into his mouth and shook him, until he began to move. When he came to, they asked him what it was like to die. He answered:

First of all, there was a roaring in my ears, then a shortness of breath, as though something heavy were lying on my chest, immediately afterwards a dizziness; next came a dense blackness in front of my eyes; then I saw flashes, as though someone had ignited gunpowder, and fired guns in my ears, but after that I knew no more.

A similar account was given by another in Holland who had drowned, but who, as Kellius relates, came to in this way: a vein was opened in his neck, into which a puff of air was blown, so that the blood affected the lungs, and they the heart, whereby it was set going. Man has aches and pains while he is sick, but when it comes to the last, and especially when he begins to take those last long breaths, he knows neither evil nor good.

Short is the road to our ultimate goal. We age early, according to Linnæus. One is an incipient old fogey at forty-two.

Stadium est ætas senilis a XLII ad LXIII, which is called *annus climactericus fatalis*, as most people die at that age. All things that have formerly been sweet and agreeable pass away; one is tired, glum, miserly and perverse; one's pulse slows down, so that if it was 150 beats a minute as a child, 80 in middle age, it is not more than 50 beats a minute at this age.

All grow old in this way; many age even earlier. He cites a misogynic passage from the seventh chapter of the Book of Proverbs:

Let not thine heart decline to her ways, go not astray in her paths.

and notes down his experience from his practice in Stockholm: *Adolescentes Holmiæ deflorati.*

It is a bleak prospect. One knows now what Linnæus means by his dismal words in the chapter on death: *Hauriamus pocula vini voluptatem.* Give wine to him who is to be made desolate, that he may forget his misery.

*　　*　　*

In this world of uncertainty the primary condition for happiness, according to Linnæus, is 'to be born of healthy parents in the most ardent sexual excitement'. Time after time he makes this observation. He himself was clearly in no doubt that his genius was due to his being the first-born of young parents. He differentiates between nature, one's vital forces, and physique, body, health. 'I have', he says, 'from my mother a tough nature, but from my father an ailing body.' The animal functions, nature itself, come from the mother, and he was fortunate in being a young woman's first-born. He draws legal conclusions from his views: 'The right of the first-born, which was a legal matter with the Jews and still is with the English, *rationem debit ipse naturæ.*' And then follows a Latin explanation to the effect that the first times of coition beget the best progeny. Nature's plan is the precept of justice, according to Linnæus.

The child's talents can be seen from the formation of the skull. 'A small brain can be in a large skull; not vice versa. The bigger the brain the bigger the intelligence; no animal has a bigger brain than man.' So far we are determined by nature. But for subsequent development the parents are responsible.

With vigour and intensity Linnæus emphasizes one's duty to nurse and safeguard the tender human plant. It is anything but the seventeenth-century orthodoxy that stamps his medical and pedagogic advice. His views on the sacrament of baptism, for instance, are not quite as full of piety as a pretty account by a later writer of how the newly born child at Stenbrohult was delivered by the christening ceremony from the clutches of death and the devil. Linnæus writes:

It is also the custom to take the newly born children to church to be christened, and that often in the severest frost, which is most injurious by reason of the cold, they being very sensitive coming from the even warmth of the womb. And it is still more dangerous when a crowd of foolish priests baptize the children in cold water, in such a way that it falls on their bare heads and causes peradventure dangerous brain fever. In Russia, a hole is made in the ice in the winter and the priest immerses the child completely, which is most dangerous and injurious; indeed, they often immerse the child so deeply that it perishes, which the mother may not bewail, but must rest content with.

This is no magical view of the sacrament's significance.

The child shall be protected from inflammatory food, and the boy from too much reading:

If one is to have good strength in old age, the foundation for this must be laid in one's youth; the results of shocks that children may receive when they are 5 or 6 years old from such causes as hunger and cold etc., are prone to remain. They should not be forced to continual study while they are yet small, for if their freedom is too greatly curtailed and their strength exhausted by study, they may indeed become clever for a time but later they will grow stupid, weak, and will not attain any great age. This can be seen with bullocks; if the yoke is laid upon them too early, they do not become sturdy beasts. Children should not consume anything acid, as it prevents growth; the same applies to puppies. Those children who early grow tall, do not live to be old, but those who hardly shoot up before their 20th year or more may be assured of a great age, provided nothing unusual intervenes. Thus it is, too, with our womenfolk, they usually grow up early; therefore they do not live to be as old as men.

Virgil, in the *Georgics* — a book which Linnæus knew well, whose spirit he could appreciate and with which he felt an affinity — exhorted the husbandman to safeguard the sprouting plantlet and tend its early days. The child is nearer to the plant than the grown-up, and moves Linnæus to accents mild and gentle. Where full-grown man is concerned his voice becomes harsh.

Habit is half nature. This is a fundamental thesis in Linnæus's dietetics. It is stressed as clearly and based on just as many philosophical and physiological reasons as in William James's *Principles of Psychology*.

On this rule is based all education and one should observe it all through life. From childhood one must be inured to much. Happy is he who receives a good *consuetudo* at the beginning and in youth, for thereby can much be learnt that in old age would be almost impossible, or at least would be a great effort; e.g. reading books, learning to play an instrument etc. are almost matters of habit. To break children of the habit of wetting their beds can only be done by fright. A good *consuetudo* in food and clothes lays the foundation of good health, and to accustom oneself to work in one's youth gives one great strength. For this reason the Romans and Greeks had their *gymnasia*, where their youth trained. Mithridates, by accustoming himself to poison from childhood, out of fear that his step-mother would poison him, was at last incapable of killing himself with poison, when he was in danger of falling into the hands of the Romans.

In *Lachesis Naturæ* Linnæus establishes this fundamental truth in phrases like hammer blows. 'When one first begins to read one soon grows tired and bored; when one becomes used to reading, one cannot drop it without a sense of loss.' But habit is not only profit. What is habitual does not tire. 'The child always marvels at the glorious light; grown-ups do not.' Wise and witty is the following distinction: 'Forwardness marries the girl, but habit the widow.' Society is built on habit. Habit enables us to endure life. 'Children who see a corpse, wonder; we who are used to it think nothing of it, although for ourselves that hour of death is the most feared of all.' But the delights of life disappear when the first drowsy wonder dies away.

Habit is well enough, but not monotony. 'When one sits in church and ponders on serious matters, one is weighed down; but never does one see a person grow heavy or sleepy at a *comœdia*, for *Harlequin* always comes along with something new.' But the way of the world is such that enforced habit at length begets disgust.

Scientists therefore become hypochondriacs.

When one's thoughts are fixed only on one thing, and one loses the taste for other sciences, it is the beginning of melancholia, for it is a clear proof of this when one science appeals more than another; one then begins to suffer no company other than those who have a liking for the same thing and cannot think of anything else, since melancholia is nought but an opinion or stubborn preference for one thing, to the contempt and exclusion of others. Yet most prone to this are those who have a pointed genius, just as a sharp pen wears down sooner than a blunt one which lasts longer.

Though a warm advocate of temperance he gives students the following advice:

A good glass of wine banishes anxiety and cheers the heart. He who incessantly buries himself in books grows pale, thin and worm-like, but he who sometimes breaks off and takes a small glass, does himself good and refreshes his mind.

The world does not like its conventions to be defied:

He who will live with the wolf must howl with the wolf. — *Wer in die Welt vorkommen wol, er brauchet meinen Rat; bald Fuchs, bald Has, bald dies, bald das; das ist ein Polizei* [*sic*]. — When Ye shall woo, it is of no avail to be learned, virtuous, upright, but droll, amusing, comical, then are Ye preferred.

In conformity with most classic moralists Linnæus contrasts natural simplicity with unhealthy luxury. The fight against extravagance was one of the chief concerns of the legislators of his time. But Linnæus is not exactly a social reformer. He demonstrates rather than remonstrates. There is at any rate no Rousseauesque infatuation in his epigrammatic and unabashed parallel: 'The lady let out a f—— at court; she grew pale and flustered, went home, died, but the Dutch skipper was unmoved by it.'

Yet he maintained that '*mores* should never be against nature'. His view is that of the doctor. 'To walk about barefoot in the heat of summer like a country wench, in a linen cloth, were very rafficient, but adieu to honneur, ambition, one were then a fool; thus fools reason.' A weak and emasculated race, high costs and poor finances are the results of luxuriance. Linnæus has written down a long list of superfluous things:

Sugar, sweetmeats, desserts.
Raisins, cinnamon, nutmeg, nutmeg-flower.
Almond cakes, jellies, carp, fish, oysters, caviare.
Preserves, mousses.
Wines, Rhenish, Cape, Tokay.
Spirits, punch, tobacco, aqua vitæ.
Tea, coffee, chocolate.
Silk, satin, velvet.
Lace.
Wall-papers, silk beds.
Drums, music!
Dancing.
Card games, backgammon, dicing.
Comedies, concerts, masquerades.
Bureaux, paintings.
Coaches, liveries, hinds, wenches.
Wax-candles, illumination.
Magnificent palaces, large windows, plaster.
So much is used up in a day as otherwise in a whole year.
Ideoque judices nequam.
Silver for China for tea, coffee, silk, porcelain, skirret, *millenos servos.*
Honour and glory shake hands.
A man is measured by the cut of his coat.
A grey jacket with virtue is despised.
All this makes one weakly.

Quite a number of things in this catalogue were certainly not without allurement for Linnæus himself; he by no means lived like a Diogenes in a tub. But apart from the tendencies of the age he had, as a medical practitioner, seen and reacted against Swedish luxury and excess. He gives vivid but repellent descriptions of the Swedish drunkenness:

Falun mining gentlemen, who in 1733 vied with each in drinking, day in day out, died after a year, but those who soon fell ill and were cured, were on their guard and lived long.

The foundry owners place the wine-firkin on the table, and the beakers go over the table and the piss-pot under the table just as fast, until the firkin is empty.

I saw Forsling unable to lie down, as the ale ran out of a full stomach.

I saw Sohlberg Eric squeeze his belly so that the ale spurted on to the opposite wall.

Not quite so drastic, but equally descriptive are the following:

The mining gentleman who is wealthy in Falun
    rises between 6 and 8 o'clock;
    breakfast: butter, cheese, meat, a nip of akvavit or a stoup of ale; goes to the mine to allot work, then into the foundry, where he smokes a pipe; goes home, takes a nip;
    dinner: solid food, meat, pork, herring or cod, and more besides;
    goes into the foundry, smokes his pipe;
    receives or pays visits at 4 o'clock, drinks well into the night 3 to 4 stoups per person;
    has a good appetite, grows fat, solid, red, burly;
    at last dies of hydropsy.

Stockholm's cavalier
    rises at 8 or 9 o'clock, dresses his hair, clothes himself;
    at 10 o'clock goes to the coffee-house, drinks one or two cups of coffee, talks;
    at 11 o'clock attends to his business;
    at 12 o'clock goes to Riddarhustorget to hear the news;
    at 1 o'clock eats, always with 1 or 2 half-pints of wine;
    at 3 o'clock goes to the coffee-house to take coffee or a glass of ale;
    at 4 o'clock pays visits;
    at 5 o'clock goes to Castenhof or some cellar, drinks a glass of Rhenish wine;
    at 7 o'clock goes to Lars on the Corner etc. to take a hazel grouse;

then gambles until well into the night, goes home, God
knows where;
at last gets the pox, ague or hectique.

Linnæus did not think highly of the Swedish people.
'*Suecus Simia*', he writes, 'for he eats like an Englishman,
drinks like a German, dresses like a Frenchman, builds like an
Italian, smokes like a Dutchman, takes snuff like a Spaniard,
tipples *akvavit* like a Russian.' But in the descriptions of the
miner's and the Stockholm cavalier's life and habits there is
more joy of narration than indignation, more humour than
moral pathos.

* * *

Many passages in the Dietetics can be read as an expression
of Linnæus's personality and idiosyncrasies. When he draws a
portrait of his great teacher Boerhaave, a free and unconven-
tional man who kotowed neither to kings nor princes, who
took no notice of kinsfolk or neighbours and whose garden
was his paradise, one sees that, to Linnæus, this seems the ideal
way of living. And when he speaks of nostalgia, which 'arises
only from innate love of one's birth-place', one can be certain
that he is thinking of Stenbrohult. And when he says with
a sigh that he 'would never have thought that conversation
could cause so much falsehood, fornication, strife, etc.', it is a
fairly safe guess that he had been plagued by old wives' tales
at close quarters.

He often betrays the fact that he was a man with strong
imagination, touchy nerves and delicate senses. A confession
such as this is of biographical interest:

Children are frightened by grown-ups telling them of the
bogey standing by the window in the dark, that they are not to
go out at night, that they must be quiet. This gives them a
fear of the dark, so that they dare not go out at night,
and if they do their hearts pound, they tremble, fearing that
someone will seize them. No reasoning helps. I myself
never dared go out alone before I was 20, and still shudder
in certain rooms, although I know better; *licet melius intellexi.*

He reacted violently to sensations both of pleasure and displeasure. He was no gourmet, but only a person with a very refined sense of taste can write as Linnæus does of the pineapple: 'have one of the very tastiest fruits in the whole world — Apricosum saturated with Rhenish wine'. A happy disposition but there is another side which suffers from that which is unappetizing and evil-smelling. When speaking of foodstuffs he dwells with most tiring prolixity on the effect they are liable to have on the odour of our bodily secretions. When for instance he talks about asparagus, he mentions nothing of its particular palatability, but in forceful and expressive words he touches on certain of its after-effects. When he gets going on subjects of this kind he sometimes makes one think of the gloomy Jonathan Swift, similarly equipped with a sensitive organ of smell.

A family interior such as the following confirms this impression of his sensibility, his delicate nervous system: 'My wife gets a headache when it is blowing outside, though she does not know it. I do not feel so well, cannot say *quomodo*; will preferably lie down.' This nausea which he cannot describe or find medical terms for, to which he is subjected when there is a high wind, this indefinable feeling of tiredness, is characteristic of nervous people.

It cannot be said that the *philosophia humana* outlined in *Lachesis Naturæ* and the lecture-notes is particularly bright or poetic. But lyricism blossoms even in the Lachesis manuscript the moment Linnæus can turn his back on the human world and speak of natural seasonal matters out in the countryside. A passage such as this, descriptive of spring, is almost as enchanting as that in *Calendaria Flora*:

The warmth of spring is temperate, neither too cold nor too hot; all things seem to come to life.
One stands in the sun against the wall; lapping up the sunshine; all horses, cattle etc. etc.
Man seems to get new life, and all things are exhilarated.
The insects, which have lain dead, are given new life.

In Holland in April the swallow comes on 6th, the cuckoo on 10th, *luscinia* on 12th, *betula* on 16th.
The swallow comes up from the lake (April 10th-15th) when the birch puts forth its leaves.
All birds twitter and all fish play.

It is not a completed poem, for it is only mnemonic jottings for a lecture, but it is the rough draft of a poem. Graphic as a picture by an old Dutch master is the description of the biting winter cold:

The house-timbers snap in the cold as though from hammer-blows.
Horse-dung leaps on the ground.
The ice cracks, rifts are made, the going is heavier.
The water-pail, raised in the air, freezes in granules before it is lowered again.

* * *

Philosophia Humana deserves to be called Linnæus's dietetic doctrine on account of its contents, its comprehensive scope, its deep knowledge of the conditions and changing phases of human life to which it testifies. But the philosophy of life forming the background is not humanistic. It is that of the natural scientist and doctor. It is rigidly deterministic. One is sometimes almost tempted to call it materialistic.

Splendid, but in its bleak naturalism somewhat cold and ruthless, is the outlook on human love-life which is developed in the lecture-notes. The physiological way of looking at things is carried out with strict logic. It is indeed a far cry from the dissertation on the floral nuptials, so full of poetry, to this presentation of the human nuptials.

The *genitalia* of plants we regard with delight, of animals with abomination, and of ourselves with strange thoughts.

When *genitura*, the seminal fluid, rises in the human body it evokes *venus*.

Now the girl acquires lustrous and moist eyes and as it were a half œdema below them, there being so great a difference in them as in a precious stone and a base metal, for prior to *annos pubertatis* they look dark, but as soon as she has reached the age of maturity one can see vividly in her eyes that desire has begun. She then begins to be gayer and more amusing, and when she sees a handsome young man, she grows still prettier and more comely, for then a *halitus incalescentis concupiscentiæ* begins to rise within her, which comes from the *genitura* which is then collected. But so soon as she loses this, she becomes an old woman and wretched, nor has she any longer her charm and *flos virginitatis*.

Excess of desire we might perhaps ascribe to the affections, but, says Linnæus, this is due far more to one's bodily make-up. If certain families are more wanton than others, it is a result of their inherited constitution. With women punished for unchastity it can be stated that on account of a peculiarity in their make-up blood is conveyed to their *genitalia* to an unusually high degree. The concepts of chastity and unchastity, which in those days theologists, moral philosophers, and jurists considered it their special duty to define more closely, are, according to Linnæus, simply a physical disposition.

'If one who is hungry or thirsty gets a dram or other spirituous things in him, he dares with drawn sword and bared breast oppose the very bravest, were he before a poltroon; so is it also *in venere*.' *Genitura* incites the youth to marriage as liquor the warrior to contempt of death, and 'women, when they are *nubiles*, go with bared breasts, to show that they have already reached *ætatem nubendi viro*, for if the breasts are large, the *genitalia* are also large; thus they are scarcely visible on a child, whose lower parts are also small'. When *genitura* presses, mania is induced. When 'girls in this state meet a man whom they like, they get chlorosis, grow green in the face, indeed often leap into the lake and drown themselves'.

Unhappy are those who are tormented by thickened *genitura*, for this passes with its *halitus* through the whole body and destroyes many a person.

It was this vapour that drove Hercules and Sardanapalus to sit by the distaff among the women. This it was that drove Samson to reveal his strength to Delilah and sleep in her lap. This was the cause of the emperor Vitellius's father's becoming so entangled in a slave-girl's net that he licked her spittle and mixed it with balsam and rubbed it on his temples. This vapour took Lucretia's life in Rome. We need not seek so far for examples, for they are to be found in almost every farm. Such a love takes away one's appetite, makes one pale, deprives one of sleep and bodily powers etc.

The surest remedy for such a mania is marriage, and in a special chapter Linnæus puts forward his advice and experiences concerning *conjugium* or wedlock. They are not characterized by an over-idealistic view. One should first and foremost beware of the ailing:

He who buys a lame horse and takes unto himself a sick wife must take the consequences, for much time is wasted by the receiving of inquiring visitors, and everything one has is spent at the apothecary's on medicaments, besides the fact that all is confusion in the house. One is also in danger, through transpiration, of attracting her wretchedness to oneself.

One should also take care not to choose one who is already up in years. Several times, both in *Lachesis Naturæ* and in the lecture-notes, Linnæus commends King David's example. Contact with youth promotes health. 'If one has a cold and is put to bed between two young people, one quickly recovers.'

Merely to look at a girl's outward appearance is to marry *par amour* (any more spiritual kind of *amour* Linnæus finds it hard to imagine). This may well be in accordance with nature, but can, the way society is constituted, be disastrous. 'To marry *par amour* is civil and natural enough, but the husband must procure household utensils and other necessities, which for one who has but recently gained employment, seems rather precarious. Moreover, it would seem as if it must go ill for a poor man who takes a poor girl for her beauty, for *sine Cerere et Baccho friget Venus.*'

Thus, according to Linnæus, the most important prelude to the holy state of matrimony should clearly be the ascertaining of the future father-in-law's financial position. And this is consistent, for with *genitura* both comeliness and love vanish. Even Venus is at best shortlived.

In a hazardous world tranquillity — calm, free contentment — is the highest good. The lecture-notes close with several pieces of moral advice, with a warning for arrogance, with a reminder of Nemesis.

*　　*　　*

In the last part of *Lachesis Naturæ* Linnæus states as a summing up of his *Philosophia Humana* that existence is a struggle of all against all:

I saw mankind consume all animals, all plants and all earth.
The beasts of prey lived on herbivora.[1]
The birds of prey lived on small birds, which ate seeds and
    worms.
The plants lived on the soil.
Hence I went first to the soil, where it all began.
The humus under a microscope was only *desumta animalia
    et plantæ*.

Linnæus has arrived at the same result in many other of his theses. But the ultimate goal takes on a darker tone when the starting-point is human life.

Linnæus often quotes the Bible, but in most cases the Old Testament. Only very seldom does he quote Christ himself. He does so, however, in one place in *Lachesis Naturæ*. It is the Song of Lament over Jerusalem, when the Saviour's voice for once is reminiscent of Ecclesiastes. Linnæus has interspersed the Bible quotations with Latin commentaries. It sounds like an antiphony, and is rather lovely.

If thou hadst known, even thou, at least in this thy day, the
    things which belong unto thy peace! — *Corporis caduci-
    tas. Nosce te ipsum. Superbissima bulla, e spumantis
    libidinis bulla.*
But now they are hid from thine eyes. — *Creditis, juvenes,
    sanitatem esse perennem.*
For the days shall come upon thee — *Anni et senectus, post
    juventutem; pauci 50 annos.*
that thine enemies shall cast a trench about thee — *Morbi,
    senectus morbus. Omnia priora cumulantur novis.*

<hr>

[1] Evidently written in mistake for carnivora.

and compass thee round — *Morbus morbum excipit.*

and keep thee in on every side. — *Omnia peccata recrudescunt, concurrunt.*

And shall lay thee even with the ground — *lecto affigere.*

and they shall not leave in thee one stone upon another — *ne quidem ossa cohæreant.*

because thou knewest not the time — *quoniam nolitis addiscere minus cavere.*

of thy visitation. — *dum ego doceam. Felix quem faciunt aliena pericula cautum.*

So shall it be with us. Few people have listened so attentively as Linnæus to the tolling of death's bell. But his piety grows out of his sense of mortality just as strongly as it does from his joy in beauty. Everything is the war of all against all. But God is therefore great who can govern it all, as it says in the *Epilegomena* to *Lachesis Naturæ*: *Ergo Deus magnus, qui gubernaret omnia.*

★   ★   ★

Accounts of and quotations from *Lachesis Naturæ* do not give a picture of a coherent philosophy. Nor is there one. But it does perhaps give an idea both of the man and his point of view.

Here, as in other Linnean writings, the beginning and the end, Alpha and Omega, are an apostrophizing of God. But this God possesses more of the concept *fatum* than of the concept father. He is not unlike Spinoza's God, *Deus sive natura.* But about reconciliation and redemption Linnæus does not inquire.

To a most surprising degree Linnæus is free from both tradition and convention when he speaks of human relationships, even to the extent that he does not seem to have been appreciably influenced by contemporary authors. In his view and utterances on vanity, he often reminds one of the older moralists, but only where general points of conformity dictated by the subject are concerned. He speaks with his own voice. He thinks his own thoughts. He approaches the world of men as he does the kingdom of Flora, and testifies only to what he himself has seen; with just this difference, that he finds Flora's kingdom more fair. His way of thinking is logically naturalistic. This naturalism is coloured by his piety, but his piety is not Christian.

Among quoted literature is the *Historia Vitæ et Mortis* by Francis Bacon, published in London in 1623. What Linnæus really read of Bacon in the original is impossible to say; but a child can see that he follows Bacon's line of thought. If he read Bacon's essay on horticulture his heart must have been filled with joy. It is worthy of mention that Bacon used the term *philosophia humana* in order to characterize the medical viewpoint of the human individual.

In one or two places in the lecture notes Paracelsus is mentioned. In one instance it concerns the secretory organs of birds; in the other, the medicinal effect of vomiting. The only conclusion to be drawn from this is that when Linnæus dipped into the writings of Paracelsus he restricted himself to their wealth of empiric observations; their mystical philosophy he quickly skipped. In this connection, too, he acted as though he had been Bacon's pupil.

CHAPTER XI

CURIOSITAS NATURALIS

IN the papers of the Royal Academy of Science for the
year 1739 there is a short monograph by Carl Linnæus
called 'On the Lappland Reindeer's Gadfly Stings'. It
deals with a gadfly, already described in *Flora Lapponica*,
which lays its eggs in the reindeers' backs, thereby causing
them great suffering. During his journey in Lappland Linnæus saw reindeer who

were so stung by gadflies that the blood was dripping off them.
Besides this, the mosquitoes tormented them persistently, and
that so severely, that they would come home daily and lie
down by the Lapp's hut, where they delighted in the smoke of
his fire made from fungi: This enabled the reindeer to have,
for a short space at least, some peace and relief from this cruel
foe's constant attacks.

Nothing, Linnæus goes on, is

stranger than that a small fly can compel the strongest oxen
and swift deer to hatch out and nurture their young, so that the
cattle or the animals often lose their lives thereby. This fly or
gadfly (œstrum) torments and plagues the cows in the summertime so grievously that they must run and leap all day long,
with their tails aloft, like the most fleet-footed deer, though
they are often so discomforted after a long and lean winter
that they are like skeletons when they first come into the fields
in the spring. They thus have a far harsher fate than the
wagtail (*motacilla*) or the lesser white-throat (*curruca*) which
may have to hatch out the cuckoo's eggs, for they are occasioned
no particular pain or torment in so doing.

From these concrete observations Linnæus passes on, as so
often elsewhere, to general natural philosophic reflections. At
the beginning of the eighteenth century there were two English
thinkers, Shaftesbury and Mandeville, who gave expression to

two radically opposed conceptions of the essence of nature which gave rise to discussion for a whole century. The one, Shaftesbury — Platonist, romantic, pantheist — saw in nature's beauty and expediency a manifestation of the Deity. The other, Mandeville — a stern and gloomy realist — contended that nature squanders life in its cruelty and rapacity, that we live in a world where one creature devours the other and which is completely devoid of moral values. It cannot be proved that Linnæus himself read either Shaftesbury or Mandeville, but it is certain that all through his life he puzzled over these questions. And to the very last he looked reality in the face just as free from illusions as was Mandeville, but was led to glorify nature's harmony and the Almighty who had created it, in the manner of Shaftesbury.

Having described how cruelly the reindeer are tormented by the gadflies, Linnæus is inspired to this hymn:

Here one could with wonderment discern the Creator's great masterpiece. How he has protected these delicate flies and made them hairy, like the Lapp in his jacket, that they might not freeze to death in these cold, northern, snow-covered mountains.
How God has provided abundant nourishment for their young, the whole winter long, in the reindeer's warm blood, like a fœtus in its mother's womb. How God has insinuated these wretched creatures into their winter quarters in an all too favourable manner, by placing them inside the skin and outside the muscles of the body, in a temperate place where there is neither too severe heat nor cold. How God has selected the reindeer's back for this purpose and not its flanks or belly, so that they cannot be crushed when the reindeer lies down.

On reading this one's first thought is that this God apostrophized by Linnæus certainly seems to have had great consideration for the gadflies but little for the tormented reindeer. Such ideas, however, were foreign to the author of the monograph, and a certain effort is required on our part to understand what he meant. First and foremost, one must try to realize that the pious clergyman's son from Stenbrohult was in one respect —

and a very important one — more ignorant of Christian morality than the many blasphemers and atheists of the nineteenth century.

According to Charles Darwin, the whole process of nature is a cruel and ruthless struggle for existence. From this he himself concluded that the occurrence of reality can teach us nothing about God. On the other hand, others have said that this occurrence teaches us that there is no God. Some have maintained that the process of nature in its cruelty is a great and glorious thing and that we should take it as a model and prototype, and organize society in accordance with the law of the jungle — to the gratification of the flaunting tiger natures. This conception has played no small part in recent German and Italian political ideology. But what these differing opinions have in common is that one perforce morally values the natural occurrence. Whether one reacts against it in horror and anguish of mind, or whether one applauds its mercilessness as Nietzsche did, one's starting point must be an affirmed or denied will (acknowledged in denial and allied to christianity) morally to value natural facts.

But Linnæus did not acknowledge these theories, or rather he did not know of them. He had learnt from Arndt's *The True Christianity* that nature's wealth, diversity, beauty, and ing ‹uity testify to God's omnipotence. When even as a boy he read Aristotle's *Historia Animalium*, he felt, one dares to assert, the impact of revelation when he began to sense that coherence in nature is God. He also learned from Aristotle that the greatest bliss and the greatest virtue is *teoria*, understanding of and insight into the essence and laws of existence. With an ecstasy whose expression was often that of a poet yet a poet whose mentality was first and foremost that of a scientist, Linnæus had made his observations and formulated his system. What he had experienced seemed to him wonderful, so wonderful that there was no room left for any moral reaction.

If one may use Schiller's terminology, Linnæus's view was naive; ours is ineluctably sentimental. It is easy for us to follow Linnæus when, in his early youthful writings, he praises the floral nuptials; but it is more difficult to see eye to eye with him in the thesis *Politia Naturæ* when he extols with the same rapture the creative power that so ingeniously maintains the balance between the different forms of life by its divine decree: war of all against all. To Linnæus, man was not an exceptional being in the sense that his individual destiny was worth weighing against the coherence of the whole. He writes thus of man in *Politia Naturæ*:

Man, nature's last and most distinguished servant, to whose advantage and convenience almost all things are subservient, also maintains the balance of nature in many cases. The colossal whales in the ocean can scarcely escape his power; the fierce and ravenous beasts of prey, such as lions and tigers, he is forced to keep within bounds in order that he himself may enjoy peace; wherever there is an abundance of plants, trees, fish, birds and animals, he knows how to use them to his own profit. In this way he maintains a seemly balance, so that nothing which is unprofitable may increase too much. But even man himself is subject to this same natural law, although I know not by what intervention of nature or by what law man's numbers are kept within fitting bounds. It is, however, true that the most contagious diseases usually rage to a greater degree in thickly populated regions, and I am inclined to think that war occurs where there is the greatest superfluity of people. At least it would seem that, where the population increases too much, concord and the necessities of life decrease, and envy and malignancy towards neighbours abound. Thus it is *a war of all against all!*

The factual statement we have no reason to oppose; we have read Darwin and we also read the daily papers. What we do not understand is that Linnæus can be carried away by it and conclude with an exclamation of thanks and praise: *Soli Deo gloria!*

This much only is it easy to comprehend: that this God of Linnæus's does not seem to have much in common with the one Christ taught us to pray to as the Father. When one reads the Linnean songs of praise to the God made manifest in nature, who so ingeniously awakens and strangles life, indifferent to suffering, when one reads Linnæus's splendidly simple, moving, and factual descriptions of the process of man's decline, so painful for those concerned, so essential to the whole, and sees how Linnæus, especially in man's physical decay and senility at the early age of 40, finds a decisive token of the almighty Artist's mathematically calculated counterpoint, one seems to see in this God a Moloch crushing trembling bodies in their death throes beneath his car of triumph, a Saturn consuming his own offspring, and one thinks that Linnæus would have done better to replace his ecstatic hymn to the Being of Beings — *Ens Entium* — with the desperately defiant words written down by Frederick the Great:

> Rien ne fléchit ce Dieu, ni les prix des offrandes,
> ni l'odeur des parfums; il est sourd aux demandes
> des mortels écrasées par ses cruels decrets.

But — *mirabile dictu* — the truth is that even the sour and cynical old king in Potsdam was almost modernly sentimental compared with the divinely gifted Swedish genius, Carl Linnæus.

There are two adjectives which Linnæus uses very often in his nature notes which have both lost their value with the passing of time and have now acquired a totally different meaning. One is *artful*, the other *curious*. It is important that we understand their Linnean significance. *Artful* is used in its original, literal sense, i.e. full of art, and also has the latent meaning of astonishing and interesting. *Artful* in the Linnean sense is a plant such as *Impatiens noli tangere*, well known to most people who have had anything to do with garden flowers; at the slightest touch its seeds are thrown out in an artful manner, that is, in a startling and uncommon way.

The word *curious* has a deeper and more serious meaning. Curious is the butterfly's development from caterpillar to chrysalis, from chrysalis to winged beauty, curious are life's laws, curious is the divine order of the stars in their courses.

For the young Linnæus the day was spent in observing what was artful and curious in nature and the night in meditating on its hidden significance.

And in this way he arrived at a concept which he called *Curiositas Naturalis*, curiosity concerning nature, conceived in the word's original meaning of thirst for knowledge. It was a passion with Linnæus, which had nothing to do with what is good and what is evil, what is misery and what is happiness, but only what actually *is*. But this attribute of 'being' became, in Linnæus's idea of the universe, something so wonderful, something so lovely, that no border-line could be fixed between the scientific assertion and the aesthetic rapture, nor between religion and the sensation of beauty. In 1748 he wrote in his thesis *De Curiositate Naturali*, which — and in all fairness we should add: not without reason — aroused grave misgivings in theological quarters:

It should therefore be more than clear as daylight that natural history is surely the most distinguished of all sciences, and the one most worthy of man's devoting all his work and energy to, since it is no less than a divine science. It reveals not only the reason why man has been created, but also the straight road to knowledge of his Creator's majesty, all wisdom, omnipotence, omniscience, and mercy, without which knowledge he cannot enjoy to the full those benefits for which he has been created by God.

The investigation of these works of God is what we should pursue. He has brought us into this world which is furnished and adorned with an illimitable diversity of nature's products. That this our earth, together with all that is on it, has been created for man's sake, is a view generally embraced by the theologians. Let us therefore not set aside God's works, but, guided by them, revere the Master! Let us therefore proclaim Thy wonders, O Lord, and let the race praise Thy astonishing power! In a word: the contemplation of nature gives a fore-taste of heavenly bliss, a constant joy to the soul and a beginning of its complete refreshment, and is the highest point of human happiness. When the soul partakes thereof, it is as it were awakened from a heavy torpor and wanders round in the light, losing itself, spending its time, so to speak, in a heavenly land or an earthly heaven.

Linnæus's extreme wrath over the theological criticism which *De Curiositate Naturali* evoked was no doubt partly due to the fact that this time he had really done his best to speak a language which he thought would please the theologians. In other variations of the same theme Linnæus does not speak of a heavenly knowledge or of a life other than this. One misunderstands him if one tries to make him a religious sceptic in the nineteenth-century meaning; there is nothing to indicate that he ever questioned the dogmatic system he had inherited from his ancestors; but it hardly influenced his way of thinking; it did not even disturb him to the extent that its antithesis was a problem for him. The number of times he mentions the Saviour's name can be counted on the fingers of one hand; and when Linnæus in *De Curiositate Naturali* speaks of a knowledge of nature as being a foretaste of heavenly bliss, he means by this something that has more to do with Aristotle than with Christianity. In most cases he is prompted to religious devotion by showing how the law of transience applies also to mankind.

'All flesh is as grass.' It is a biblical saying that Linnæus loved to quote, and he has even tried to prove its truth in a literal meaning: man's flesh, his brain and his heart, are transformed in the grave to grass. And this transformation was, in Linnæus's eyes, miraculous, curious. In his natural system he ascribed to man, in one respect, a unique position. The Christian teaching that creation existed for man's benefit he consciously affirmed in so far as he believed that it lay in man's power to reach the stage when hard reality acquired a meaning. It was vouchsafed to man to comprehend hard reality, establish its conformity to natural law, and thereby be filled with rapture. God created man that he might admire His work. And for the attainment of this goal all that is required, according to Linnæus, is knowledge of nature and nothing else. He who observes the artful and meditates on the curious must fall down on his knees in wonderment when face to face with the ingenuity, the will for beauty and the might of the omnipresent Artist.

All flesh is as grass, and life is suffering and violence and perfidy. But for Linnæus life was designed, above all else, for the practising of the greatest virtue, *curiositas naturalis*. In his address on *Deliciæ Naturæ*, or The Delights of Nature, given when the ennobled Carl von Linné for the third and last time laid down his chancellorship, when he was broken and bitter and tired, and was himself soon to demonstrate the law of transience through mental and bodily decay, he spoke once more of the artful and the curious:

The strange story of the monkeys.
The vampires, who suck blood from the sleeping.
Putorius, which defends itself with a deadly stench.
Didelphis, which lets its young hide in its stomach.
Pecora, with its 4 different stomachs.
Hippopotamus, Behemoth and its element.
The whale, the largest animal, with its young.
The griffin, which comes rushing down like a thunderstorm.
Orpheus, who sings a song of divine beauty.
The water starling, which dives into the seething rapids.
The great grey shrike, which warns the birds of the hawk.
Chavaria, which grazes with the hens against birds of prey.
Psophia, who sings with its mouth and gives resonance with *posteriora*.
The cuckoo, which is hatched by other birds and fed by them.
The swallow, which hibernates at the bottom of the lake.
The peacock, which is the most gorgeous of all.
The pelican, which draws water.
Diomediæ, who can neither fly nor walk.
The honey-bird, which is the smallest and gilded.
Boas, a snake, which can swallow a whole ox; is 20 to 30 ells long.
Rana cornuta, which is the most frightful of all to see.
The crocodile, Leviathan and its ravages.
The siren, who sings in the water.
Torpedo and the Electric Fish, which give electric shocks.

The gold fish, which is like molten gold.
Callichtys, which goes from one pond to the other.
The thrift of spiders and many insects.
Mussels, which eat the very stone.
Gordius, which goes through clay as a fish in the water.
And many more without end.

What does this enumeration signify? It has nothing to do with what is good or evil, just or unjust, blissful or painful. It concerns something that to Linnæus was much more important: what was strange and inscrutable. And its contemplation and observance filled his mind with awe.

No Swede — and only one or two among the thinkers of Europe — has had the faculty of freeing himself from all human valuation, all the importunate claims of feeling, as Linnæus did in his attitude to nature. He followed Apollo. His character has been greatly misunderstood by those who have said that his scientific outlook was narrowed by his clerical inheritance. Linnæus followed Apollo into spheres so icy that his detractors' moral, political, and cultural bombast would instantly have frozen in them.

Swinburne has spoken thus of the Hellenic god:

> Yea, is not even Apollo, with hair and harpstring of gold,
> A bitter god to follow, a beautiful god to behold?

If one is sometimes reminded of Spinoza when reading what Linnæus has written concerning his general view of life and the universe, this signifies of course that the creative power hailed by Linnæus is more like Spinoza's *Deus sive Natura* than the God whom Christ called Father. There is, also, in Linnæus's own attitude to all the bloody and agonizing spectacles of nature a trait reminiscent of Spinoza. There is a submission, a piety, which is filled with both theoretical and aesthetical ecstasy, but which also implies a moral placidity.

This does not mean, however, that Linnæus ever read or even dipped into Spinoza's writings. Generally speaking, he seldom read any modern authors other than those of importance to his natural scientific research. He simply had not the time.

There were no spare hours in his busy working-day when he could read merely for pleasure. His need of beauty he satisfied with Virgil and Ovid, his devotional requirements by reading the Bible. The fact that Spinoza's name had not a very good ring in people's ears, even as late as the 1730s, would not have prevented Linnæus from studying him. In point of fact, Spinoza's name was revered by the only authority Linnæus really looked up to among his contemporaries.

For Hermann Boerhaave was a Spinozist. This Dutch physician and natural scientist, to whom Linnæus so often paid homage and whom he regarded as a model and a master, had originally been intended for the church. It was his acquaintance with Spinoza's philosophy that caused him to abandon theology for natural science. One cannot say for certain that such was the case, but it may have been that Linnæus, during his numerous conversations with Boerhaave, also imbibed doctrines derived from Spinoza's *Ethica*.

On the other hand it *is* fairly certain, as has already been indicated, that when Linnæus speaks in his thesis *De Curiositate Naturali* about the observation of nature being a foretaste of heavenly bliss and a constant joy to the soul, he does so under the influence of the thinker, Aristotle, to whom he owes, more than to any other, both his system of natural science and his philosophy of life in general.

In the 7th chapter of the 10th book of the *Nicomachean Ethics* Aristotle says:

If then of all the actions in accordance with the various virtues those of policy and war are pre-eminent in honour and greatness, and these are restless, and aim at some further End, and are not choiceworthy for their own sakes, but the Working of the Intellect, being apt for contemplation, is thought to excel in earnestness, and to aim at no End beyond itself, and to have Pleasure of its own which helps to increase the Working; and if the attributes of Self-Sufficiency, and capacity of rest, and unweariedness (as far as is compatible with the infirmity of human nature), and all other attributes of the highest Happiness, plainly belong to this Working, this must be perfect

Happiness, if attaining a complete duration of life; which condition is added because none of the points of Happiness is incomplete.

In the 8th chapter of the same book Aristotle goes on to describe how this perception, this *teoria*, must be regarded as heavenly bliss:

And that the perfect Happiness must be a kind of Contemplative working may appear also from the following consideration: our conception of the Gods is that they are above all blessed and happy: now what kind of Moral actions are we to attribute to them? those of justice? nay, will they not be set in a ridiculous light if represented as forming contracts, and restoring deposits, and so on? well then, shall we picture them performing brave actions, withstanding objects of fear and meeting dangers, because it is noble to do so? or liberal ones? but to whom shall they be giving? and further, it is absurd to think they have money or anything of the kind. And as for actions of perfected self-mastery, what can theirs be? would it not be a degrading praise that they have no bad desires? In short, if one followed the subject into all details, all the circumstances connected with Moral actions would appear trivial and unworthy of gods.
Still, every one believes that they live, and therefore that they Work because it is not supposed that they sleep their time away like Endymion: now if from a living being you take away Action, still more if Creation, what remains but Contemplation? So then the Working of the Gods, eminent in blessedness, will be one apt for Contemplative Speculation: of all human Workings that will have the greatest capacity for Happiness which is nearest akin to this.[1]

At the end of the same chapter Aristotle says that 'he who works in accordance with, and pays observance to, Pure Intellect, and tends this, seems likely to be both in the best frame of mind and dearest to the Gods'.

Linnæus was accustomed to these thoughts from his school-days. Is it unreasonable to think that one often hears in his words a direct echo of the *Nicomachean Ethics'* proclamation

[1] These two extracts are from the translation by D. P. Chase.

that Contemplative Speculation is life's highest aim? And *Curiositate Naturali* is by no means the only Linnean work which inclines the reader to this point of view.

Of course there is also a difference; the God of Linnæus is the Old Testament's God of Creation; when Linnæus speaks of observation he also means, among other things, invocation. But the observation of nature, which he considers to be life's object, has a purely theoretic side, and it is through this that Linnæus in his philosophy of life approaches the *Nicomachean Ethics*. The Linnean observance of nature implied knowledge of life's coherence, of *systema naturæ*. It had, finally, an aesthetic side. In the Linnean wonder at the riches of creation the religious, the aesthetic and the theoretical all combine.

In the introduction to Lectures on the Animal Kingdom it is said that everything is done for the sake of mankind. It is quite a usual dogma in Christianity, but in its application Linnæus comes nearer to Aristotle than to the Bible. He goes on:

But one then asks, why is everything in the whole world created solely for the sake of mankind? He dies and is subject to corruption the same as all the other animals and natural things. What greater qualities has he? Namely these: that not only can he see, hear, smell, taste, and feel, as they do, but he can also regard the strange compounding of all natural things, fathom their curious qualities, and therefrom form a conclusion of their high and wondrous Master.

Linnæus has varied this theme in a long line of dissertations. In *Œconomia Naturæ* he has asserted, in a description brimming with detailed observations of nature, that the struggle for existence in nature merely shows the harmony of the whole.

If we wish . . . to seek the purpose of nature's arrangement whereby some animals have only been created for the torment and destruction of others, there opens up before us a glorious spectacle of God's wisdom.

Even Arndt could have said this, and similar things have often been proclaimed from the pulpit in Protestant churches.

But Linnæus went a step further. It is not the cosy optimism of the Theodiceans, according to which man, in the best of all possible worlds, is so unimaginably well placed, that colours the Linnean natural philosophy. He is thinking little of man's comfort when with great enthusiasm he cites the poisonous snakes as an example of the Creator's wonderful power (Preface to King Adolf Fredrik's collection of natural-history specimens):

The weapons with which the Lord of Nature has armed Himself are terrible: to the snakes, which he has cast on the ground like naked fish, without feet, wings or fins, and which might therefore most easily of all be destroyed, he has given their poisonous barbs, but in order that these might not do too much damage he has only so armed every tenth kind, and has given them no distinguishing mark so that men and animals must go in terror of them all, not being able to distinguish the armed from the unarmed. One is horrified at the mere thought of the qualities of these murderous weapons. When the Indian poisonous snake (*Coluber Najas*) bites, there is not time enough to say an 'Our Father', and when the rattle-snake (*Crotalus horridus*) bites at a considerable age, there is no appeal.

Passages such as these deter one from associating Linnæus with other preachers of the world's expediency, to whom it would never have occurred to praise the rattle-snake as one of the Creator's masterpieces. The Linnean view of nature implies a conception of life according to which man's life and death is only of secondary importance compared with *curiositas naturalis*.

There is a particularly moving passage in Linnæus's fragmentary *Iter ad Exteros*. He is describing the frogs croaking on the plain of Holstein:

The frogs croaked quite loudly, 3 to 4 times louder than in Sweden, and had their own tongue. Some sang here, that life seemed to be reborn; I know of no grief that would not be banished; some so badly, that one might have died of melancholy.

This particular example is chosen because most people are deaf to the pleasantness of frogs' croaking; and the amphibians were, as is known, otherwise despised even by Linnæus. One senses behind the words an almost breathless astonishment at the immeasurable wealth of physical reality. When Linnæus is in the act of describing it, tormenting questions lose their sting.

He sees reality as it is. He does not fight shy of facts. He never closes his eyes to sights that may be depressing. If a person from above were transported to our earth, he asks in the treatise *Politia Naturæ*, what would he see?

He would see all these animals not only gorging on the most beautiful flowers, but also mercilessly tearing each other to pieces; in a word, he would see nothing but a war of all against all, and furthermore feel himself so defenceless and exposed to threatening dangers from so many quarters, that in his uncertainty and perplexity he would scarcely — and not even scarcely — be capable of finding a place where he could feel himself really safe.

This might seem terrible. But the *curiositas naturalis* of Linnæus is *jenseits von Gut und Böse*. The word that is nearest to this conception is wonder. It means the thirst for knowledge that is never quenched, and Linnæus had it. It also means surprise, admiration, a feeling for the richness, beauty, and infinity of existence, and this too Linnæus had. Englishmen sometimes say that the finest thing about Shakespeare was his faculty of *wonder*; among us Swedes Linnæus is the one who in this respect comes closest to Shakespeare.

Is it being presumptuous, if one has called the theoretical side of Linnæus's *Curiositas Naturalis* Aristotelian, to call its aesthetic side Shakespearean? It is of course only in the same sense that allows, for instance, a literary historian like Sir Walter Raleigh to call the politician Burke the English prose writer that most resembles Shakespeare. Had Linnæus read Shakespeare he would have been able to choose Shakespearean quotations as suitable mottoes for the group of dissertations whose contents have been dealt with in this chapter. They would have been more appropriate than the quotations from the Bible he collected in *De Curiositate Naturali* and which in the context seem so strange and so arbitrarily interpreted that one can well understand the astonishment of the theological faculty at such an exegesis. If one wished one could also say that the dissertations and descriptions of Linnæus contain Swedish equivalents to the highlights of Shakespeare's poetry.

> Night's candles are burnt out, and jocund day
> stands tiptoe on the misty mountain tops —

the Swedish equivalent can be found in the *Journey to Lappland*. Lorenzo's whisperings to Jessica of how

> . . . soft stillness and the night
> become the touches of sweet harmony

resemble in Swedish tradition the Linnean songs of praise to the incomprehensible riches of earth and the canopy of heaven. Shakespeare's cogitation over the seeming pointlessness of everything, over the cycle of matter, over the jarring disharmony between human passions and the indifference of events — much of this is to be found in Linnæus, though with different emphasis. And even the same hard-won confidence, the same reliance behind the assertion of life's cruelty. Even the belief in Nemesis which was to set its stamp on the ageing Linnæus's thoughts, Shakespeare has formulated clearly and concisely; it is in Edmund's speech in *King Lear*:

> The wheel is come full circle; I am here.

To quote again from *De Curiositate Naturali*:

What is our life, I want to ask, of which we are so afraid? We are not ignorant of the fact that death, which is to draw a line through everything, will one day come upon us and cannot be avoided; none the less the coming days seem to us so pleasant that we consider we cannot wish for anything better than to add several more to those already behind us, but a like enjoyment we also experience from the time that has gone. Thus — nought but dreams and vanity! The works of many thousand people are, often enough, to be considered, during a single revolution, as having never existed. When the Caliph Omar in the year 640 subjected Egypt to his sway, which after the Battle of Actium in 660 had bowed down to Rome, and the emperor Amru occupied Alexandria, the famous and extremely rich Alexandrine library was burnt down, and 700 thousand volumes, composed with much toil and sweat, were turned to flames and ashes.

It is therefore manifest that all our work is subject to decay. Therefore, we should learn to understand what God's purpose was at the time of man's creation, when He saw to the propagation of the species and the protection of the individual. This His purpose will be quite fulfilled when the happiness and glory is gained by us that during our appearance on this worldly stage we can join in songs of praise to the glory of the Creator's omnipotence and His mighty works.

This is no solid optimism. 'We are such stuff as dreams are made on ... ' But in the dream we can, thanks to *curiositas naturalis*, learn to know a divine will, and this knowledge gives the dream a meaning.

CHAPTER XII

THE ORIGIN OF THE SPECIES

IN *Philosophia Botanica* Linnæus laid down as a fact in 1751 that the number of species is the same as the number of forms created from the beginning: *Species tot numeramus, quot diversæ formæ in primitione sunt creatæ.* The sentence was to be read as early as 1736, when *Fundamenta Botanica* was printed in Holland. The wording is very definite. When the theory of evolution became common property during the latter half of the 1880s, these words were cited as proof of how exceedingly out of date the Linnean systematism was.

If one reads a little further on, however, it will be seen that Linnæus himself sides with the natural scientists who doubt that this statement can be proved. And it would have been odd if he had not done so, for even when he wrote his *Critica Botanica* in Holland he had, as we have seen, reckoned with the so-called monstrous forms, albeit at that time he was only willing to assign them a kind of phantom existence beside the natural species.

In 1742 an Upsala student had found near his home in Roslagen a plant that he was incapable of classifying. He pasted it into his herbarium, and in due course it was shown to Linnæus, who at first thought it was a *Linaria*. But the flowers seemed rather strange, and Linnæus began to suspect that an alien inflorescence had been pasted there to hoodwink the botanists. The plant turned out to be genuine, however. Its root, stalk, and leaves accorded in all respects with *Linaria*, but the flower was different. Linnæus described it more fully in the dissertation on *Peloria* published in 1744.

Linnæus considered he could affirm that the plant had been produced from *Linaria*, yet it was a new species, even belonging to another class than *Linaria*. He gave it the name of

Peloria, from the Greek word *pelor,* meaning malformation, monster. He writes:

Nothing can be more extraordinary, however, than what has happened with this plant, namely that the deformed progeny of a plant which has formerly produced irregular flowers can bring forth regular ones. It thereby diverges not only from its maternal family but also completely from the whole class, thus providing an example of something that is without parallel in botany, so that by reason of the flowers' dissimilarity no one can any longer recognize it. This is indeed no less extraordinary than if a cow gave birth to a calf having a wolf's head.

Linnæus at that time was still convinced that the hybrids of the plant world as well as those of the animal kindgom were incapable of reproducing themselves. But *Peloria* did so, and hence follows, he writes, 'the extraordinary conclusion that it is possible for new species to arise within the plant world; that families with dissimilar fructification organs can have the same origin and character; why, even that in one and the same family there can exist different fructification organs. And by reason of this the whole basis of fructification would be demolished, and the basis for all botanical science, and the natural classification of plants be exploded.'

Linnæus realized only too well that the point of view he had put forward in the first edition of *Systema Naturæ* had hereby received a knockout blow; but he was not one of those who value their own theories more than the truth; generally speaking, he was one of the least dogmatic scientists there has ever been, always prepared to reconsider things, always willing to pay regard to and bow to facts. But in this matter he still hesitated; he did not as yet rightly understand where this new discovery would lead him — and natural science.

In the accounts of Linnæus's journeys written during the 1740s one notices several times how the geological observations lead him outside the boundary of his original conception of creation; one critic has attached so great an importance to the theories concerning dizzy perspectives of time that he considers the 1740s saw the emergence of an evolutionary geological conception in Sweden. But one should draw a distinct line between the modern conception of evolution — in the sense of development from lower to higher — and the Linnean thoughts regarding a very slow change. In his address on the growth of the habitable earth — *Oratio de Telluris Habitabilis Incremento* — given on the occasion of the conferring of doctor of medicine degrees in 1743, he develops the thought that the earth, in the dawn of creation, was covered by 'the vast ocean with the exception of a single island in this immeasurable sea, on which island all animals could comfortably have their being and all plants most excellently thrive'. For originally there existed only one hermaphrodite plant and one pair of the bisexual animals; these first links in the series were God's direct creation. But any change or fluctuation in, any blending of, the series of species, he was unwilling to speak of here. Even in the preface to the work on King Adolf Fredrik's collection of natural-history specimens in 1754 Linnæus does not budge from this view. It should be taken into account, however, that this preface was to a certain extent written *ad usum delphini*. He says of the origin of species:

That the dry land is extending more and more is so incontrovertible that the whole of nature, hills and dales, fossils and earth's strata, the abyss of the sea and all stones, would speak of it were all else silent. Just as the earth is now increasing, so has it also in a certain proportion formerly enlarged itself with the dry land, and if we trace back this increase, we stop at a little island.

If we also trace back, as already mentioned, the increase of all the plants and animals, we stop at a single one, where two have become one. Thus on this little island there was a living museum of natural-history specimens, so that among all the plants and animals now to be found on the earth there was not one missing. Here, therefore, the first man had everything that could be obtained from nature for human use and pleasure, and he has consequently been the happiest. Should this first happy man have had, as we have had, to learn everything in nature through his outward senses, he would of necessity have to scrutinize each and every animal's nature, form, and qualities in order that he might distinguish them by particular marks and names. So the first man's duty in the garden of bliss with its complete natural-history collection, was to regard the Creator's work.

Here Linnæus, as the second Adam, hails his predecessor from paradise; the conception is purely biblical; the species are given by their Creator once for all. On the surface there is in this work from the year 1754 the same static idea of the universe as in the first edition of *Systema Naturæ*. But only on the surface. Doubt was merely suppressed for the time being.

*   *   *

Carl Linnæus at this time was in a state of perplexity, which may well be understood, as the problem was a puzzling one. Towards the end of the 1750s he seems to have been filled with strange thoughts. The most important work on the subject from this decade is the dissertation on the transmutation of plants, *Metamorphosis Plantarum*, discussed in Upsala in 1755. It deals chiefly with the fixed metamorphoses within the plant world compatible with Linnæus's original conception of species, but also with what Linnæus calls monstrosities and varieties. The most daring passages in the work are these:

It is said that Réaumur caused a rabbit to fertilize a hen. The eggs produced chickens which were exactly like ordinary fowls except that they were covered, not with feathers, but with fine hair. This experiment is admittedly relevant up to a point, but we dare not draw any general conclusion from such cases. The most frightful conclusions could in fact be drawn from this; as far as mankind is concerned one would have reason to think that the Moors had a rather strange origin — something that I for my part, however, am unwilling to ascribe to them. ·

How are these words to be interpreted? At a guess one would say that Linnæus for fun propounds one or two paradoxes which in the name of reason he instantly rejects. Does he mention the Moors', i.e. the negroes' pedigree merely to show how preposterous the thought really is? Even so the expression would be remarkable, for as far as I can see Linnæus does toy — admittedly half in jest — with the thought of man's descent from the apes. The very thought of a cross between rabbit and hen would be enough to appal the author of *Systema Naturæ*. A hybrid is a monster, it is true, but if nevertheless it does exist, then perhaps . . . It was dangerous to complete the thought. It was still more dangerous to express it. Linnæus had no wish to get drawn into a heresy case.

I am convinced, however, that these lines in *Metamorphosis Plantarum* have a much greater significance for the appraisement of Linnæus's way of thinking than one would suppose from his other works. My reason for saying this is a hitherto unnoticed letter from his son, Carl von Linné the younger, written to his father's great friend, Bäck, on September 8th, 1778, preserved in the manuscript collection of the Royal Academy of Science. A German theologist, Zimmermann, just after Linnæus's death had accused him of having been an atheist. Zimmermann writes, the younger Linné says,

somewhat harshly of my late father, and makes him out to be an atheist; it is not possible for a *naturæ historicus* to be an atheist. Even those who deny the word and the manifestation cannot deny nature, which gives the most convincing proof of the Creator, and the further one probes into this the stronger becomes conviction. Never was my late father an atheist; no, the reverse; he could never endure to hear people talking in this way; his collection of Nemesis surely testifies to his conception of God, and so do other of his works, and particularly the preface to the System. He believed, no doubt, that *species animalium et plantarum* and that *genera* were the works of time: but that *ordines naturales* were the works of the Creator; if the latter had not existed the former could not have arisen.

As an example of such 'species of time' Linné the younger mentions the very hybrid between rabbit and hen dealt with in *Metamorphosis Plantarum*, and then goes on:

My father's conception of the world was this, I think: that when this globe first existed, a small point on it was bare, and there creation began.

Then follows in the younger Linné's letter a description of the creation and multiplying of plants and animals closely according with what his father had written in the above-mentioned dissertation on the habitable earth's growth.

The interesting thing about this statement is that the elder Linnæus clearly should have accepted in later years the idea of any hybrids at all being 'species of time'. Linné the younger also speaks of hybrids between hoofed and cloven-hoofed animals. Creation, the divine and original, applies only to the natural orders; that is, within the animal world for instance, the anthropoids (man, ape and, according to the scheme in *Systema Naturæ*, sloth), rodents, birds of prey, aquatic birds, etc.; within the plant world the natural orders, e.g. lilies, grass, palms, but not the sexual system's classes and genera. But when Linnæus does not hesitate to acknowledge the existence of hybrids between different natural orders, such as rabbit and hen, is it not likely that the thought of hybrids within the anthropoid animals' mutual order, which in *Metamorphosis Plantarum* was propounded as a paradoxical fancy, as a kind of *reductio in absurdum*, in reality did not seem so very preposterous to Linnæus towards the end of his life?

But this solution of the question of his conception of the species problem does not mean that Linnæus thought in terms of evolution. The differentiation of the animal and plant world through blending of the species is not the same as evolution.

To determine exactly the nature of Linnæus's thoughts is clearly impossible, as it is unlikely that he ever determined them for himself. They were revolutionary thoughts. In 1759 the Imperial Academy of Science in St. Petersburg had announced a competition for the best answer on the question of whether new proofs or experiments could be produced confirming or refuting the doctrine of the plants' sexes. Linnæus competed and to avoid the risk of losing the first prize he gave, in his usual unconstrained way, the so-called anonymous entry the motto *Famam extendere factis*, known throughout the world of learning as Linnæus's special motto, used, in fact, as his seal, among other things. And of course he did receive the prize;

but one of the erudite adjudicators commented that he definitely made a reservation against Linnæus's 'brilliant rather than correct views' concerning partly questions of heredity, partly experiments with hydrids.

In the Linnean competition entry, which was given the title 'New Proofs of the Sexuality of Plants', it says that in several cases there can be no doubt that one

has before one new species, produced by cross-fertilization. From all this we learn that the bastard offspring is the image of the mother as regards the inner medullary substance or fructification organs, but of the father as regards the leaves and other outward parts. This, therefore, lays a new foundation, on which natural scientists should be able to erect a great building. From this it would seem to follow that the many species belonging to the same family were in the beginning a single species, and that they have since arisen through such cross-breeding.

Linnæus then speaks of a number of different *Geranium* species, which might easily

lead botanists to suppose that within the vegetable kingdom the species within the same family are an equal number of forms, which have sprung from a single species through the marriage of the flowers, also conversely, that a family is nothing else but the summary of those plant forms which derive from the same mother but different fathers. Yet— whether all these species are the children of time, or whether the Creator from the very beginning of the world has restricted this course of development to a definite number of species, I dare not decide with certainty.

It is somewhat cautiously and dubiously written. Here he seems to think that the genus within the plant world is a constant on the maternal side, but differentiated by separate paternal influences. In the matter of biological construction Linnæus discriminates between medullar substance, of medulla or pith, inherited from the mother's side, and cortical substance belonging to the bark, apparent in the plant in the shape of the leaves and stalk, inherited from the father's side. But these theories have no connection at all with Linnæus's experience of *Peloria*, which in its cortical substance accorded with *Linaria*, but differed from its origin in its medullar substance.

In a letter to Bäck of September 4th, 1764, Linnæus has tried yet another formulation of this somewhat elusive law of the formation of the species:

One must suppose that God has made 1 before he made 2, 2 before 4; that he has made first *simplicia* and then *composita*, that he has first made one species of each genus, that he then mixed different genera, from which derived several species. Suppose that God has made a *ranunculus*; that this species has been crossed with *helleboro, aquilegia, nigella* etc. *per generationem hybridam lege divina concessam*, and that *proles* in these crosses between the plants, just as between animals, have retained *medullare* from the mother and *corticale* from the father. From this have derived so many species *ranunculi foliis hellebori, alia foliis aquilegiæ, alia foliis nigellæ*. All these may not be distinguished in *arbitrella genera*; that this is so is proved *a posteriori*. This is *fundamentum fructificationis*, generally acknowledged from the time of Gesnerus.

The safest thing to say is probably this, that Linnæus never succeeded in really pin-pointing his new conception of species. But the old one, that formed the basis of *Systema Naturæ*, was utterly and irrevocably abandoned. At last he even cancelled from the new editions of the steadily swelling *Systema Naturæ* the theory that no new species arise.

One can be certain that this theoretical development cost him great pains and anxiety. The foundations of his conception of the universe had been shaken and deranged.

During the early 1750s Linnæus had completed his empiric research work. In 1751 *Philosophia Botanica* appeared, in which he confirmed and supplemented in detail the theses concerning the outer and inner construction of plants which he had formulated in his youth in *Fundamenta Botanica*. In 1753 he had finished *Species Plantarum*, which he was thenceforth to regard as his foremost work. In it he had accomplished the subsidiary nomenclature and arranged and described all the plant species then known to exist. In 1758 a new edition of *Systema Naturæ* appeared, a consecutively ordered fourth edition of massive proportions, with subsidiary nomenclature even for the multitude of newly discovered animal species.

To all editions of *Systema* he had appended a preface, which increased in size with each new edition. One Linnean authority has shown how Linnæus, without much consistency of thought, has generally drawn his natural philosophical theories from several different quarters, chiefly from Seneca. These general observations are perhaps rather to be regarded as embellishments, as a decorative preamble — just as dissertations at that time were frequently adorned with verses in Latin, French or Swedish.

In the edition of *Systema Naturæ* published in 1766, which was called the twelfth, but if reprints are discounted was only the fifth, there are, however, a number of original reflections in the preface which seem not a little puzzling. Linnæus here puts forward a purely mechanical conception of life:

The animal [he says amongst other things] is an hydraulic apparatus deriving from marrow, *perpetuum mobile*, burning like a Vestal fire with ethereal-electrical flames, maintained by the breath, in which an inconceivable freedom of will resides.

Linnæus continues his interpretation of life's entity in a still more singular manner. He says that in the animal machine or apparatus there are five departments of faculty (*facultatum cameræ*); these he illustrates with various symbols: equilateral triangles in different positions, both whole and split, and a circle.

One authority writes concerning these symbols that 'I have been unable to interpret them, having regard either to their derivation or their meaning, and the definitions which accompany them are almost equally incomprehensible'.

One need not, however, heed this criticism. The symbols are originally chemical formulae — used also as philosophical signatures — and occur in other Linnean writings, especially in the *Lachesis* manuscript; in the order in which Linnæus has them they mean spirit (*gens anima*), life, water, earth, and the principle of generation. The definitions are less easy to understand. In the seventeenth century an Italian by the name of Giovanni Borelli, in his work *De Motu Animalium*, dedicated to Queen Kristina, had tried to apply the physical-mathematical principles to biology; it is more this line that Linnæus follows here, but he distorts the theories and unconcernedly mixes Cartesian rationalism with cabalistic expressions.

It is a sign of weakness, even if one allows for the fact that Linnæus always regarded these prefaces more as rhetorical feats of strength than as scientific résumés.

Within a chaotic science he had created a cosmos. The species were still clear in his concrete outlook, but his natural philosophy went astray in a murky labyrinth. In *Systema Naturæ* of 1735 the world was firm and bright. In *Systema Naturæ* of 1766 its foundations were shaken. With his conception of species demolished, night once more brooded over unfathomable depths.

CHAPTER XIII

THE FORTUNES OF LINNÆUS

O N March 22nd, 1763, Linnæus sat down and wrote a
letter to his brother and sisters far away in Småland.
As so often before, when the longing for his native
countryside beset him, his thoughts dwelt on the words of the
exiled Ovid:

> By what sweet charm I know not the native land
> draws all men nor allows them to forget her.

He thought also of his own strange destiny. He had lately
acquired a name other than the one he had borne, which his
brother still bore, and with which he still signed this letter;
he was now von Linné. In the letter he takes a retrospective
view of his life:

I have been doctor, professor, royal physician, knight, and
nobleman.
I have been vouchsafed to see more of the Creator's wondrous
works, in which I have found my greatest joy, than any other
mortal who has lived before me.
I have had my disciples sent out to the four corners of the
earth.
I have written more than anyone else now alive; 72 of my
own books are at present on my desk.
I have won a great name extending to the Indies themselves,
and have been acknowledged as the greatest in my science.
I have become a member of almost all scientific societies; in
Upsala, Stockholm, Petersburg, Berlin, Vienna, London,
Montpellier, Tolosa, Florence and now recently in Paris, with
honourable mention among the 8 renowned men of the world.
But when a tree has reached its greatest height, it must fall,
for *quidquid ad apicem pervenit, ad exitum properat.*
This last year I have noticed how age is hastening on me, for
when the watchmen begin to tremble, the strong to stoop, the

millers become few and the gold chain runs out, then is our life on the wane; when the climate grows cold and the leaves pale, and the flowers vanish, then is winter on the threshold. I have begun to put my house in order.

Linnæus has written often and in detail of his life and his fortunes in his many autobiographical notes and sketches. Few Swedish writers have busied themselves with their destiny with such an intense interest and so diligently counted up, over and over again, their life's collected assets. Linnæus began writing autobiographies when still quite young; he went on doing so until he was a broken-down old man.

As with other memoirs, Linnæus's autobiographical notes are not always reliable; where days long since passed away are concerned his memory plays him false, and things and forms, events and people, assume proportions at variance with those they once possessed. But the Linnean memoirs have all the greater value as an expression of what he thought and felt at the moment of writing them. He is very candid, and often brilliant as a stylist; private memories and his own fate seemed to inspire him.

They are instinct with a strong assurance, a very definite consciousness of the importance of the Linnean life's work. An eminent authority on Linnæus's various autobiographical documents asserts, however, that nothing testifies more plainly to the depth and sincerity of Linnæus's piety than this very feeling of having a divine mission to fulfil. For my part, I can only see that mixed with this vocational awareness are often other sentiments, which suggest not so much gratitude to the Creator as what one might call worldly conceit. Linnæus was a man in whom gay and gloomy moods and desires followed each other in quick succession. But were one to choose a comprehensive expression for the feelings animating Linnæus's descriptions of his own destinies, the word 'wonder' would seem the most apposite, the same word previously used to characterize the Linnean attitude to nature. When dipping into *Handwritten Memoranda on Carl Linnæus, by himself*, old Gustav Vasa comes frequently to mind, for during his last years he would dwell with undiminishing wonder on the meaning of his destiny, at once humbly grateful and patently proud of its greatness.

The most important of these Linnean confessions have been collected by Adam Afzelius under the title of *The Fortunes of Linnæus* and published in 1823. It has often been quoted, but we make no apology for doing so again:

God himself has led him with his own almighty hand.
God has caused him to sprout from a stump, transplanted him in a distant place, caused him to rise up to a goodly tree.
God has inspired him with such a burning desire for science that this has become the most pleasant of all.
God has ordained that every desirable means should exist in his time to enable him to win progress.
God has guided him in such a way that what he has wished for and not gained has been to his greatest advantage.
God has made him accepted by *mæcenates scientiarum*, even by the highest in the land including the Royal Family.
God has given him advantageous and honourable service, the very kind he has most wished for in all the world.

So the description of the fortunes of Linnæus continues. Family relationships and distinctions are described in much the same way as in the letter to his brother and sisters. But the greatest happiness has been in his science, his life's long research work:

God has suffered him to peep into his secret cabinet.
God has permitted him to see more of his created work than any mortal before him.
God has bestowed on him the greatest insight into nature-study, greater than anyone has gained.
The Lord has been with him, whithersoever he has gone, and has exterminated all his enemies for him, and has made him a great name, like unto that of the great men of the earth (2 Sam. VII: 9. 1 Chron. XVII: 8).
None before him has pursued his profession with greater zeal and had more *auditores*.
None before him has made more observations in nature-study.

None before him has had a more solid insight into all the three kingdoms of nature.

None before him has been a greater *botanicus* or *zoologus*.

None before him has so well *historiam naturalem patriae*: *Floram, Faunam, itinera*.

None before him has written more works, more correctly, more methodically, from his own experience.

None before him has so totally reformed a whole science and made a new epoch.

None before him has arranged all the products of nature with such lucidity.

None before him has corresponded so extensively over the whole world.

None before him has sent out his disciples to so many parts of the world.

None before him has written his name on more plants, insects, in fact on the whole of nature.

None before him has seen so many of the Creator's works, and so thoroughly.

None before him has become more renowned over all the world

So much is certain, at all events — Linnæus was not one of those who doubt themselves or the significance of their achievements. It would be hard to find more unstinted admiration of his importance than that he himself expresses here and in many other places. A religious feeling also exists, admittedly, but it is rather egocentric. He is grateful to his Creator, but although not uttered in so many words the thought is always there that God's blessings towards him have indeed been justified; if he has been chosen before others, he has also known better than anyone else how to put his talents to profitable use. Humble gratitude and proud assurance go side by side.

But at the height of his life's achievements, with this imposing perspective to gaze back on, with a fortune which he himself considered greater than other people's, Linnæus was yet unhappy. Shortly after he has regarded the magnitude of his attainments with an almost giddy feeling, reflected on his election, delivered thanks to his Creator as a firstling of God's work, Ecclesiastes' words on the vanity of all worldly things ring again in his ears. With all his fortune he was of mortal clay, doomed soon to be dissolved.

Linnæus, as we shall see in a later chapter, has mused greatly over the sin of arrogance, called by the Greeks *hybris*. It testifies to his self-knowledge, among other things. He was not unfamiliar with *hybris*. But he recognized his shortcoming and strove, though not always with success, to suppress it. He went often in fear of rebuff and this is the only explanation of his extreme susceptibility, his horror-tinged reaction to the slightest reverse, the mildest criticism. Prophets often have this characteristic; when they grieve at the world's lack of appreciation it is because in their success they see a corroboration of the righteousness of their mission. But, being the peculiarly rich-minded and versatile person he was, Linnæus could also take an objective view of his achievements and resolutely declared that fortune was neither to be valued highly nor passionately desired.

Beside the comprehensive verbal portrait he has given us of himself there is in his literary remains yet another, in all respects the contrast of his own, but painted with the same conviction. It is the commemorative address on a university clerk and fellow, Andreas Neander, a man who was never accompanied by fortune.

The deceased had been one of Linnæus's close friends; he had amongst other things, witnessed his will. In life he had been a plodding and energetic labourer in the vineyard of science, tardily promoted, poor, ascetic, god-fearing. In his address over him Linnæus improved the occasion by saying that fortune and happiness is fleeting and of little worth; virtue is all. His speech, in all its seeming artlessness, is nobly phrased and very moving, but one wonders whether the man who was foremost in Linnæus's thoughts when he wrote down these exhortations was not himself.

He speaks of Fortune:

Fortune, fleeting Fortune, she gives and takes wrongful possessions which her event has occasioned; had fleeting fortune given anything to him, I would cast it on the fire; but she has been but a strict stepmother to him. But what honest virtue has bestowed on him, that is his. Of that no one, *rerum vicissitudines*, can deprive him.

Here and, as we shall soon see, even more plainly later on, Linnæus depicts Fortune as a frivolous wanton, while Virtue is the one worthy of respect, the only desirable one in this transient world.

Fortune dispenses her gifts so strangely; some mortals she drives forward, others she holds back. After he had made himself proficient in the world of science and been crowned with a master's laurels he thought to receive some fruit from his labours; but, as in the time of Solomon, it is of no avail that one discharges one's duties well; all depends on time and fortune.

He treats of Neander's many vain attempts to gain reasonable advancement:

Accordingly, he tried 20 times, the 10th and 20th alone succeeding. Thus it was in vain for him to get up early and go late to rest, for others received their fortune while they slept. Dear God what it costs one, after having devoted all one's best time and years to diligent work to acquire some skill, to see oneself at the end and in old age forgotten by a beloved country, and others undeservedly preferred.

And so Linnæus exhorts the students to make their choice.

You see [he says to them] that when man walks in the bright sunshine he has a double shadow following closely on his heels, however he turns and wherever he goes. To these two shadows I liken man's two familiars: Virtue and Fortune, which constantly follow, attend and lead him; the darker shadow is Fortune, and the brighter one Virtue. However cloudy the day, yet are these two shadows always in attendance, whether they are visible to us or not.

These two servants of man, I said, accompany us whether we walk or ride forward across this world's arena.

They are quite different in disposition and being. Fortune, the world's angel, is vivacious, transitory, sumptuous, featherbrained and fickle; when we hand her the reins she drives recklessly over stones and logs and usually ends by throwing us out, either into a ditch so that we drown, or against some stone, so that we perish miserably. Virtue, God's angel, on the other hand, is god-fearing, meek, prudent, considerate, and steadfast; when we hand her the reins she drives us most carefully and protects us from the smallest stone, so that we journey as safely as on our feet over this world's slippery roads. It is at God's discretion, or often our own, to hand the reins to whichever we please. He is the more prudent who hands them to Virtue, though this makes Fortune envious. The late Neander handed them over unreservedly to Virtue, as we can see from the whole of his earthly journey.

It is the simple virtues, the unpretentious ones, the ones not always so highly valued by the world, which Linnæus goes on to praise in Neander. He speaks of his modesty, his equable temperament, his obligingness and courtesy, his neatness and thrift. By dint of the strictest diligence, by caring well for what he possessed, he gained not prosperity but a livelihood. He was also esteemed even 'by people of condition'. He grew learned, though he 'did not excel'.

Fortune never gave him so much as a glass of her nectar.

Thus, gentlemen, when I would pour out his cornucopia for you, it is quite empty. Here are neither titles, escutcheons, stars, estates, families nor any other gaudy ostentation. But when on his grave I pour out his horn of virtue, you see fall the bright flowers which never lose their lustre and never wither, namely piety, diligence, neatness, virtuousness, obligingness, and the Imperial crown of honesty. Go your ways and pick like flowers for yourselves.

It is brilliantly spoken. It is deeply felt. It is very sincerely meant. And at least some of the contents in Virtue's horn could also have been poured out on Linnæus's grave. But the 'gaudy ostentation', the title, the escutcheon, the star, the estate and (what is most surprising of all in this list) the family, all this was Linnæus's fortune, which in his autobiographical notes he has so many times enumerated with such gratitude and pride. These very things, his status as professor, his ennobled rank, the Order of the North Star, his estate and other property, the wife he desired and thriving children, he used to write that 'God had honoured him with'. And here he calls it gaudy ostentation.

Was he afraid of his fortune? Did he want to disarm Nemesis? Linnæus praised Neander for having been a zealous church-goer. 'He never missed a Sunday or other holy day in present-ing himself with the crowd who praised, magnified, and wor-shipped their God. He went to the Cathedral however cold the winter. He never arrived late; never left the church before Divine Service was quite over.' It has been said that Linnæus resembled Neander in this respect and therefore praised a golden rule which he himself so closely observed. But if one can believe what a well-known zoologist has related of the Linnæus family traditions, Linnæus praised instead just what he did *not* do. He is said to have behaved in a very overbearing way in the church of Danmark, taking his dog with him to divine service. As time went on the dog was the only one to represent the gentry from Hammarby, and then it interrupted the sermon by yelping. When the interpreter of the Word complained of this, Linnæus is said to have answered that the preacher should take the dog's barking as a hint that he had gone on too long. If this be true, one can find in the words about Neander's being so punctilious in never leaving the church before the service was over another hidden self-reproach.

It is an unusual disposition into which one gets an insight when studying simultaneously the Linnean autobiographies and the speech over Neander. Linnæus harboured great contrasts within himself. Seldom has anyone put forward plans of life which are apparently so at variance with one another.

And these conflicting characteristics were reflected in his writings. The strict objectivity in the dissertations on *Curiositas Naturalis*, on the economy of nature and the politics of nature, is in seemingly direct contrast to the manuscript which he entitled *Nemesis Divina*.

CHAPTER XIV

NEMESIS DIVINA

THE word Nemesis in the history of religion has two different meanings. It is of great importance that they be kept apart. On the one hand, Nemesis is the force that maintains the balance of existence: when fortune has attained her fullness, she vanishes; pride, *hybris*, goeth before a fall. On the other hand, Nemesis is the representative of justice and revenge.

The first-named conception is the older of the two, but they both have their origin in pre-Christian times.

One encounters the idea of Nemesis as representative of avenging Justice on Hellenic ground in Aeschylus' conscious polemic against the older Nemesis belief. It occurs in the first part of the *Oresteia*. Immediately prior to King Agamemnon's entrance the Chorus sings a song whose last three stanzas are as follows:

A grey word liveth, from the morn
Of old time among mortals spoken,
That man's Wealth waxen full shall fall
Not childless, but get sons withal;
And ever of great bliss is born
A tear unstanched and a heart broken.

But I hold my thought alone and by others unbeguiled;
'Tis the deed that is unholy shall have issue, child on child,
Sin on sin, like his begetters; and they shall be as they were.
But the man who walketh straight, and the house thereof, tho'
        Fate
Exalt him, the children shall be fair.

But Old Sin loves, when comes the hour again,
To bring forth New,
Which laugheth lusty amid the tears of men;
Yea, and Unruth, his comrade, wherewith none

May plead nor strive, which dareth on and on,
Knowing not fear nor any holy thing;
Two fires of darkness in a house, born true,
Like to their ancient spring.

But Justice shineth in a house low-wrought
With smoke-stained wall,
And honoureth him who filleth his own lot;
But the unclean hand upon the golden stair,
With eyes averse she flieth, seeking where
Things innocent are; and, heeding not the power
Of wealth by man misgloried, guideth all
To her own destined hour.[1]

To us moderns, to us Christians, this seems an old and
familiar thought, even though presented in an unusually
monumental way. But the Athenians who listened to the
words of Aeschylus in 458 B.C. undoubtedly thought otherwise. To them it was a new and revolutionary idea, so new that
most of them probably did not quite grasp its meaning. This is
even intimated by Aeschylus himself: he begins by saying that
'a grey word liveth, from the morn of old time among mortals
spoken'; against this he wishes to lodge a protest, he alone:
'But I hold my thought alone and by others unbeguiled.'

What people believed, what all the Greeks believed, was, as
Aeschylus says, that when fortune reaches her fulness there
follows endless woe. This was the Greeks' conception of
Nemesis, and for them it had no other meaning. This faith
was not founded on a subjective sense of justice, but on objective observation. It lacks any moral justification. Fortune is
followed by misfortune; it applies equally to the just and the
unjust. 'For one thing good the gods give mankind two that
are evil,' says Pindarus. 'Know thyself' was inscribed on
Apollo's temple at Delphi; meaning that man should be aware
of his limitations and realize that no permanent happiness could
fall to his lot. Bliss is the prerogative of the gods, and they are
careful to see that no mortal has any lasting share in it. The

[1] Gilbert Murray's translation.

great, the mighty, the happy arouse the envy of the gods and are sooner or later seized by their wrathful hand. But those who live unpretentiously in a corner can more easily escape misfortune; they are not struck down so often by the deadly thunderbolt. Care is taken to see that the trees do not grow up into heaven — Goethe's words may be said to summarize the Greek belief in Nemesis.

It cannot be said that this Greek piety is at variance with our experience of the way of the world. Not always, in fact very seldom, is the path made smooth for the just and rough for the unjust; it should be so perhaps, but it is not so. But even if we do not believe it is the work of the gods, we must recognize the objective accuracy of the Greeks' belief that all overweening aspiration is followed by a fall. Life's first lesson is that no happiness endures for long. It was neither actual conditions nor historical observations which engendered revolt against the Greek belief in Nemesis in one or two minds. It was not reason but the moral feeling which the original Nemesis belief excluded. The Greek gods, as the common people imagined them, behaved in fact like the powers by whom earthly life for an unpresuming observer seems to be controlled. Their only shortcoming was that on closer inspection they did not appear so wholly awe-inspiring. It is in man's nature not to rest content with what is, but also to inquire for what ought to be.

The genuine Greek piety in its oldest form is encountered in the tragedies of Sophocles. King Oedipus is struck down by disaster through no fault of his own; the chorus that brings the drama to a close merely stresses that the fate of the once mighty monarch who is now so utterly broken proves that no mortal should be counted happy as long as he wanders on earth. It is Sophocles' guiding faith; it is reflected in a pure disposition, and in the tragedies is suffused with a poetic glow. That is why it does not always occur to us that it has nothing in common with what we usually call a moral outlook.

It is therefore this Greek faith that is referred to in *Agamemnon* as living 'from the morn of old time among mortals spoken'.

But Aeschylus holds his thought alone, and his opinion — which the Greeks thought strange — was that only godless deeds are followed by disaster, and that in the lineage of the just good fortune shall be lasting. Thus he too has a belief in Nemesis, but as distinct from that of his countrymen it is based not on objective observation but on a subjective sense of justice. In other words, his Nemesis is a moral divinity. Of Justice he says that it 'guideth all to its own destined hour'. This Nemesis has points of resemblance to Jewish and Christian conceptions of a righteous and chastising God.

It has been said of Aeschylus' *Agamemnon* that it is less comprehensible to us moderns than Sophocles' great play. It would be more correct to say that the strange thing about *Agamemnon* is simply this, that the deepest thoughts of the work are much more akin to our way of thinking than the ideas dominating the older Greek literature. *Agamemnon* is the first great attempt in Greece to give the train of worldly events a moral justification.

The gods who, according to Aeschylus' conception of the world, guide the destinies of men, must therefore be different from the envious and suspicious inhabitants of Olympus who resemble us humans. Three strophes from another chorus in *Agamemnon* tell us from which conception of divinity the new morally justified belief in Nemesis is derived:

> Zeus! Zeus, whate'er He be,
> If this name He love to hear
> This He shall be called of me.
> Searching earth and sea and air
> Refuge nowhere can I find
> Save Him only, if my mind
> Will cast off before it die
> The burden of this vanity.
>
> One there was who reigned of old,
> Big with wrath to brave and blast,
> Lo, his name is no more told!
> And who followed met at last

His Third-thrower, and is gone.
Only they whose hearts have known
Zeus, the Conqueror and the Friend,
They shall win their vision's end;

Zeus the Guide, who made man turn,
Thought-ward, Zeus, who did ordain
Man by Suffering shall Learn.
So the heart of him, again
Aching with remembered pain,
Bleeds and sleepeth not, until
Wisdom comes against his will.
'Tis the gift of One by strife
Lifted to the throne of life.[1]

This Zeus, not the Olympic but an unknown god, forces man through misfortune to consciousness. Suffering, bestowed by his hand, purifies.

When the prophet Amos, 300 years before Aeschylus, tried to replace the faith in a tribal god easily appeased with sacrifices with faith in a righteous god, the counterparts of these divergent views of Nemesis were also opposed to one another. The Indian doctrine of Karma is a kind of belief in Nemesis. And in Greece Aeschylus was one of the first, but not the only one, to hold such an opinion. In both Hesiodos and Solon can be found utterances which recall the above strophes from *Agamemnon*; Solon in particular, in his great prayer to the Muses, has expressed a faith that the fortune conferred by the grace of the gods is safe and secure, and that Zeus is a righteous chastiser and avenger.

Within the Christian world the belief in Nemesis is to be found both in the form Aeschylus gave it and in the older form conceived by Sophocles, but if a modern person believes in Nemesis, it is more often Aeschylus with whom he agrees.

But there is one great man of comparatively modern times on whom both these conceptions of Nemesis had a very great influence. And that is Linnæus. That is why it has been necessary to try to explain their significance in such detail.

*   *   *

[1] Gilbert Murray's translation.

During the latter part of his life Linnæus dabbled in collecting examples of retribution in human life. Destinies he knew of, cases from his practice as a doctor, anecdotes and rumours he had heard, he jotted down on octavo pages; the loose sheets were kept in a little case which was well hidden away. On them he also made a note of his own reflections on life and death, as well as quotations from the Bible and from ancient and modern poets. These memoranda gradually assumed the form of a spiritual will intended for his son.

After a chequered career these notes on *Nemesis Divina* found their way to the Upsala university library. They have now been bound, and the pagination denotes the order of the pages when they were found in a private library in Kalmar towards the middle of the nineteenth century. Unfortunately this order has nothing to do with chronology. An examination of the different kinds of paper shows that the pages must have been jumbled together.

Nor is it possible to decide from the context the order in which the notes were made; by fixing the date of each event Linnæus refers to we know in any case that the relevant note could not have been made earlier. But this gives no indication of how much time elapsed before Linnæus wrote down his reflections on the events in question. It seems likely, however, that most of the memoranda were made during the 1750s, '60s, and '70s, and some, as we shall see, are probably older. From the muddled handwriting it is apparent in some cases that they were written by a man who had had a stroke, and therefore date from one of Linnæus's very last years.

The subjects touched on in these memoranda were sometimes very delicate; the whole collection has the character of a secret document. In a letter to Bäck already quoted in this book Linné the younger speaks of his father's 'collection of Nemesis' as the best testimony of the latter's faith in God; from this one may infer that Bäck too was familiar with its contents.

Linnæus dedicated the collection to his son in these words:

You have come into a world that you do not know.
You do not see the world, but wonder at its glory.
You see everything in confusion as no one has seen or heard.
You see the loveliest lilies stifled by weeds;
But here dwells a righteous God, who puts all to rights.
Innocue vivito, numen adest!

There was a time when I doubted whether God bothered about
     me;
Many years have taught me what I leave to you.
It is the wish of all to be happy, which few can be.
If you wish to be happy, then know that God sees you *ubique:*
Innocue vivito, numen adest!

If you do not believe in S.S.,[1] then believe in experience.
I have noted down these few cases I remember;
Reflect yourself on them and take care:
Felix, quem faciunt aliena pericula cautum!

I should rather have spared the names than name them,
But must to make you convinced of the truth.
Keep these secret as your eye and your heart.

Believe no one in this world; tomorrow your enemy.
Should kith and kin have known of it,
You would have persecution all your days,
And perhaps your death.

Keep it therefore as secret as I give it to you,
And this I desire of you, that none
May be harmed in name or honour.

If you err against my behest, you sin;
You filch other people's honour.
You wound your faithful father
And you will most certainly be justly punished.

For I have put down the names to convince you,
As you secretly ask about these matters.
Perhaps several stories have been wrongly told to me.
Find out; say nothing; harm no name and honour.

[1] S.S. — *scriptura sacra.*

This free verse has expressive rhythm, and the division into stanzas emphasizes the exhortations with especial force. *Innocue vivito, numen adest*; 'live blamelessly, God is near', this is the well-known Linnean motto. But here the words *numen adest* probably have the same meaning as in ancient times: they imply something sacred and secret. Linné the younger must have been grown-up by the time his father wrote these words; they could scarcely have been written much before 1770. No prophet of a secret cult could more earnestly enjoin a novice to silence than Linnæus does here. Not even the relations must get a hint of the hidden wisdom which he here confides to his son. It is clear that he himself believes it is life's darkling purpose he discloses. God's plan in nature he had been able to expose to the world. God's plan in human affairs he would expose only to his son. No gossip, no false suspicions must grow up out of this; he exhorts his son to reflect that a number of stories might have been wrongly related. Concealed from the world, but well preserved in the mind of his son, his doctrine of Nemesis was to go on living.

In order to understand the memoranda properly one should bear this dedication in mind. Certain passages, otherwise abstruse, are written with an eye to the son and his way through life.

The editions of *Nemesis Divina* which have been published give a rather incomplete picture of the original document's contents. An enormous amount has been left out for reasons of decency and tact. And it must certainly be admitted that much of the book is not suitable for print. One or two of these omitted passages must be mentioned, however, if one is to give an idea of the Nemesis memoranda. Otherwise the picture of the ageing Linnæus is not true to life.

Quite a lot of it has very little or no connection with Nemesis, with the law of retribution. Many references to the Bible, quotations from the classics and verses from Swedish poets stress the power of God and misery of man. Linnæus himself writes this simile:

I conceive mankind as so many candles. The sun illuminates the body, wisdom the soul. The world is a palace of the Almighty's wisdom. God lighted each and every soul with his fire. Thus all people shine with their wisdom in this theatre according as God has formed them; some He has made into big candles, some into rushlights. These burn as long as they last, and when they have burnt down, God puts others in their place, that they may never go out, that light may always shine. The candle can no more say that the castle is made for its sake than man can say that the world is made for his sake, but everything in its great wisdom is to the majesty of God.

It is the same conception as in his natural science writings. But although it is at sharp variance with the conventional Protestant conception that the world is created for man's sake, this Linnean doctrine leads as a practical consequence to two Christian virtues: humility and compassion. We possess nothing. It says of riches: 'All we have is a loan from God. We have nothing with us; we take nothing away.' We should also consider that all sinners lie under the ban of necessity. Linnæus says (page 156) about a farm-hand whose destiny could be read in his hand, that 'if God has written our destinies on our hands before we have been made, we should have commiseration with unfortunates such as their fate has been'. It is a thought that has not even yet managed to find its way into Swedish legislation.

Linnæus has eyes, warm and clear, for the wrongs of society and the hard lot of the poor:

The poor peasant toils the whole year, has scarcely enough straw to lie on, save what he gets from his labour; *sic vos, non vobis*. Must sell his seed for $\frac{1}{2}$ in the autumn (buy in the spring); his provision-basket is hung high up. The nobleman extracts to the last stiver, his children must starve and his wife work at the hall without food. Carts goods to Stockholm. His animals grow gaunt, his sole help. Why has God not made the master slave and the slave master? At last he is thrown out of doors with wife and child.
Yet you wonder that God exterminates the master's seed and finally makes them poor.

Think of the wretched slave who works for you while you sleep. He ploughs the field you reap. You say: it is my estate; I can do as I please. I say: nothing is yours; it is all lent to you by God.

But it is not only the idea that the right of possession and class privileges are absolute of which Linnæus wants to divest his son. He also warns him against idle endeavour. He certainly does not want to bring him up as a fortune-hunter, a careerist, a go-getter. Fathers usually instil into their sons that they should strive to go far. Linnæus stresses the reverse. Under the heading of *Industria*, diligence, he writes:

He who came at the eleventh hour received a penny just as the first.

And he confides to his successor that what he has won has not been worth the trouble.

I gave myself no peace by night or day, read, wrote, examined. What had I else? Name, empty air, annihilated by others. Note that what I have done plagiarists will make their own. Titles, empty air, nobility, knight, royal physician.

It is almost the same phrase as in the address on Neander. Linnæus has been dazzled by his fortune. But he has also been afraid of *hybris*. And he dares not urge his son to follow the same road as himself. It is better that he should work less, as long as he is shielded from vainglory. Then Nemesis will not intervene.

This is the original, the Sophoclean conception of Nemesis. It was very strong in Linnæus. It is a purely classical trait in his character and disposition. He will not teach his son to fight his way forward to honour and high office; he wants instead to teach him that it hardly pays to exert oneself. God, Fortune, Destiny, determines all. He does not want to make him successful, he wants to see him humble. He will not awaken his self-esteem, he means to inculcate him with fear and awe.

Under the heading of Fortune he writes:

Deus dat cui vult. (God gives to whom He will).

One is unfortunate from that day in all he undertakes; another everything *ex votis* (according to his wishes).

One farmer in Hammarby liberal, alert, everything sufficed; his house gay, neat. The other farmer mean, miserly, everything sour, behind in all his work. 1770 *mutatur scena* (the scene is changed). The latter farmer everything neat, gay, prosperous; the former, everything contrary.

One works and gets no further; another sits in the wishing-chair like Broman.[1] An idler rises to the highest rank; a diligent man stays in the same place and gets no further.

This is very like 'the grey word' spoken of by Aeschylus:

> That man's Wealth waxen full shall fall
> Not childless, but get sons withal;
> And ever of great bliss is born
> A tear unstanched and a heart broken.

It can also be expressed in Biblical language. Linnæus did so once in a letter he wrote in 1756:

Now I will settle down and see the world strive and hanker; but I will do nought, for it is of no avail that one is kind; it is idle to rise early and go late to rest, for God gives to His own while they sleep.

It is like the pious counsel his father Nils Linnæus wrote in his son's pedigree: *Non est volentis nec currentis sed miserentis Dei.*

This is the deepest trait of Linnæus's religiousness. But his expression of it also confirms his determinism as a naturalist. Behind all the contradictions in Linnæus, at first glance so puzzling, there is a certain unity. At times he could vary his Spinozistic conception of nature — Spinozistic even though he never knew Spinoza — so that it came very near to the Rev. Nils Linnæus's faith in Providence.

*   *   *

It was said of Linné the younger that he cared not so much for Flora as for the nymphs. It may be exaggeration or calumny,

---

[1] A well-known king's favourite.

for this young man, on the whole so amiable and engaging, was often the subject of envy. At all events, it is certain that the father, in the notes he made for the son's edification, made extremely detailed and unvarnished comments on the sixth commandment.

It was apparent from Linnæus's so-called *Philosophia Humana* that his view of love was not romantic. Nor is his conception of woman that of the troubadour. Under the heading of *Uxor* in the Nemesis memoranda he has made reference to the most misogynic quotations from the canonical and apocryphal books of the Old Testament. And his own remarks on the subject are an even more bitter wisdom than King Solomon's.

'Character of a wife who is a whore', one section is headed (page 10). The beginning of the picture looks like this.

1. She is unhappy at home; especially when the husband is at home.
2. She longs for him to go away; is displeased at his return.
3. She often alleges *menstruam* in order to avoid his visits.

Linnæus then changes to Latin, and with a lack of reserve worthy of a medical text-book, he tells of an unfaithful and loveless wife's behaviour during coition. He then goes on in sombre tones:

When she evades her husband because of weakness or other circumstances in order to please the adulterer, she loses the tender love for her husband. — A pure girl can never relinquish love of her husband unless she has consorted with others. — Result: she shares her love with the adulterer. Strange children become involved. — Must share with them that due to the rightful heirs; is thus robbed daily of all they get; thereafter never sure of his own wife, for stolen fruit tastes best.

Then comes a reference to these threatening verses from 2 Samuel xii, 11:

Thus saith the Lord, Behold, I will raise up evil against thee out of thine own house, and I will take thy wives before thine eyes, and give them unto thy neighbour, and he shall lie with thy wives in the sight of this sun.

For thou didst it secretly: but I will do this thing before all Israel, and before the sun.

The words are from Nathan's punitive sermon to King David.

There is no sane reason to conceal words such as these, but it is of great importance that they are rightly interpreted. Although it was whispered that Linnæus was prone to jealousy, which is fully borne out by his will, there are no valid grounds for assuming that Linnæus is here speaking from his own experience, or that the characteristics of an unfaithful wife have any bearing on his marriage; had this been the case he would never have chosen his son of all people as his confidant. But what he passionately desires is to warn his son against a fate which has never been rare and which was still less so during this period of Sweden's history. Possibly one is also right in taking the Bible quotations to mean that Linné the younger had assiduously sown his wild oats.

The important thing is that this expression of paternal care contributes to the characterization of Linnæus as a person. As a doctor he had seen much laxity, and he never ceased to be disgusted by it. He was of a cleanly nature. And in just the same way that he feared his son might forget God, so did he pale at the thought of his ever being married to an unfaithful wife. Few fathers think so far ahead and paint such a harshly realistic picture of a dreaded misfortune. Even other still more painful *sexualia* are mentioned with the same end in view.

Among the instances of the intervention of Nemesis which for reasons of decency no one dared publish, are many which are excellently told, which reveal a tart sense of humour, and in our day and age can hardly be considered shocking.

On page 170 Linnæus relates this pointed little story:

Hökerstedt, the Governor of Gotland, falls in love with his pretty maid-servant; solicits her a long time; she promises him secretly to come to him next night in his room, where for the most part he lay apart from his wife.

A friend of Hökerstedt pays him a visit for a few days, sees the girl, admires her beauty. The Governor says he has himself hankered after her for a long time, and that she has promised him tonight positively. His friend begs the Governor to refrain that night, as he could have all the others. Which the Governor does; they change rooms when evening comes.

Towards evening the maid-servant goes to the wife, asks to be allowed to go away; giving as the reason that the Governor has so importuned her that she has had to promise. The wife answers that she will do what she can, goes during the night in the maid-servant's place, thinking she is lying with her husband; keeps quiet, does not speak, so as not to give herself away. Notices that it is not her husband, but too late.

The story is familiar; the same or a similar erotic *quid pro quo* is a constant theme in medieval and Renaissance short-story writing, in Chaucer's *The Reve's Tale*, *Les cent nouvelles nouvelles*, in *Decamerone*, in Bandello and Margaret of Navarre. Which of course is no reason why exactly the same thing should not happen in Gotland, for there is a good deal of truth in Oscar Wilde's quip that it is reality which imitates fiction. It is clear, however, that Linnæus gave a wry smile as he wrote down this story; the very style shows this.

There is also a certain stern humour in another, somewhat darker Gotland story (page 166):

Rydén, a district judge in Gotland, had a beautiful but lewd wife, whose eye was always on young men, among whom *pastor loci* (the local clergyman) Kanutius was one. The husband gets *hectique* from anxiety; she sweeps and dusts, gives him no food, to hurry the process; he dies.

Kanutius marries her pregnant, calls the child Knut after a mariner whom he believed to be the child's real father.

She begins to drink sottishly. Kanutius is twice Member of Parliament, both times on his return home finds his house ruined and must begin anew. He thrashes and bastes her, she stews the birch to give him food.

These stories are quoted not only because they have a point. They also throw light on the question of when Linnæus began making notes concerning Nemesis. It seems to me quite obvious that Linnæus noted down these anecdotes when, at the bidding of Parliament, he made his journey to Gotland in the summer of 1741. They also have a sense of humour which is lacking in the later accounts of criminal cases; Linnæus's temper was no longer as gay, and it is also possible that the collection of examples had acquired an ever graver significance for him as it increased in size. But the date given by one critic as the one likely to be the earliest for the Nemesis memoranda should therefore be moved forward to 1741. This was the year of his son's birth; but it is improbable that this occasioned the beginning of the collection; the dedication to it dates, as has been said, from about 1770 at the earliest. It should rather be presumed that it was the exploration of the Swedish provinces which led Linnæus to collect these traditions as well as all the others.

Even during his youthful wanderings examples of Nemesis had branded his memory. On page 181 are one or two sombre reflections:

The pastor's wife in Malung whores and is unfaithful to her husband. The daughter becomes a tippler and dons her mother's shift. The two sons fight a duel, one runs the other through and goes off to Norway.

The pastor's wife in Kvickjock and Lule Lappmark whores with the regimental quartermaster. The pastor is made desperate thereby and takes to drink. The daughter becomes a whore and is tumbled by a Lapp.

The story from Malung Linnæus may have heard through his various relations in Dalarna, but his knowledge of the appalling domestic affairs of the vicarage at Kvickjock is no doubt derived from his Lappland journey. It cannot be deduced for certain that Linnæus began as early as this to collect examples of the sins of the fathers being visited on the children, but the subject did interest him, and his reflections on Nemesis can therefore be said to originate about this time.

The examples of Nemesis omitted or truncated by the publishers concern mainly breaches of the sixth commandment. They certainly give a lurid picture of the moral state of affairs in Sweden. Perhaps these memoranda helped to give him to whom they were dedicated an aversion to matrimony. In any case, Linné the younger died unmarried.

In other words, Linnæus's notes on *Nemesis Divina*, the divine justice, should be regarded as an unfinished complement to *Systema Naturæ*. These cogitations and observations have perhaps come to play too big a part in the understanding of Linnæus; they are linked up with the fact that our Linnean memories have been best preserved by humanists; but it must not be forgotten that the classification of plants in *Species Plantarum* is more essential to the comprehension of Linnæus than the moral speculations in the Nemesis notes.

One just cannot fix and define right and wrong, good and evil, in the same way that one determines a natural causal connection. Linnæus himself was certainly aware that his foundations for a coherent moral system were riddled with flaws. But although incomplete and secret, these memoranda undoubtedly had an exceptional value in Linnæus's eyes. All that was accidental, unjustified, incomprehensible in human life was to be explained in this way; Linnæus wanted to show God's eternal plan with the destinies of mankind, just as he had shown the plan with the determination of sex in the plant world or the struggle of all against all in the animal world.

It was not easy to make this intelligible; it was not something the meaning of which one grasped straight away. Linnæus asked: 'What is greatness? Nothing, when the wheel of fortune turns. What is wisdom? Knowing one's own folly. What is the possession of power? The foremost place among fools. What is the possession of riches? Being beholden to other fools. What are clothes? The livery of a comedy with which to frighten children.'

It was easier for Linnæus to see the wonderful meaning, the clear logical sequence of the animal world, where one species preys on the other and the balance is maintained. But even in his young days he began to think that there is also something in human life which is cause and effect in a moral sense, a previously determined succession between sin and punishment, an ethical natural law.

Now Nemesis has, as mentioned above, two different meanings within Linnæus's realm of thought. Nemesis is partly the power that sees to the balance of existence; the parallel to the Linnean viewpoint of the animal world is clear. According to this, the tendency of every species to predominate is limited, owing to God's wise dispensation: when deer and hares grow too numerous, they attract animals of prey which decimate their numbers; when man, feeling powerful and secure, enlarges his field of activity, a corrective power automatically steps in and crushes him in his complacency. Nemesis is also the representative of justice and revenge; it sees to it that as man sows, so shall he reap; the evil we do we are necessarily punished for here on this earth; all human actions and all human destinies are morally and causally determined, no less than the physical conditions of life of the plants.

What Linnæus means is that there is a coherent plan even in what is apparently purely accidental. He tells of the great lords and parliamentary heroes from Sweden's Age of Liberty, and tries to show that ill-gotten gains soon turn to dust, and that perfidy and violence are not only concrete actions, once done and then forgotten, but forces acting in accordance with nature in the same way as biological seeds of propagation. The evil reappears; it reappears in a mechanical and schematic way, like the effect of pollen on pistils.

Linnæus notes the following about a count and Privy Councillor's son:

Meets on the lake a farmer, who with his hind drives against the count's sleigh. The count strikes the peasant a blow over the head so that he dies. The count disclaims the matter, as the farmer had driven against his sleigh while asleep. Some years later the count is again driving over the ice. The previous night the ice had broken and made a rift. The very spot where the count falls in is the place where the farmer had formerly been dealt the fatal blow. The hind gets out easily and the horse as well. The hind tries to help the count in every way, but cannot reach him. The count calls out: I see God's vengeance in this place. And he drowns.

There is law but no gospel in Linnæus's conception of the universe. It is difficult for us today to understand Linnæus's moral attitude when noting down an event such as this:

A man saves a thief from the gallows. The same man is captured by enemies and is to be hanged. There is no rope, but the thief comes and brings a rope.

Granted that in the eighteenth century people had a different idea from ours of the necessity of hanging thieves — it is still rather forbidding when Linnæus, because he collects and systematizes such items, thanks God for having 'let me see thy secret judgments'. It should also be borne in mind that many phrases have come into existence *ad usum delphini* — with a moral purpose.

But justifiable or unjustifiable, the belief in Nemesis gave Linnæus what he desired more than anything else: a general perspective, a rational explanation of human existence. When, like Linnæus, one is partly a logical genius of outstanding dimensions, partly mistrustful, suspicious, and grudging in one's feelings, when one has such a strong love of the objective at the same time as one is afflicted with such a violent subjectivity, it is then reasonable to embrace this belief in Nemesis as a conclusive answer to the riddle of existence.

Linnæus neither could nor would leave any questions unanswered. In this he reveals his genius, his greatness as well as his naivety. He writes in the Nemesis notes:

What is it I feel within me? I do not see it. The eye is a *camera obscura*, it depicts the objects, but of the affected nerve I see nothing, thereof I can judge nothing. The nerve leads to the brain, where I see nothing.
There is, notwithstanding, someone who perceives, who calculates, what I do not know. Is it strange that I do not see God, when I do not see the I which dwells within me.

What is it that acts, operates, moves the heart, intestines, nerves? Nothing moves of its own accord. What is it that causes a cleansing vomiting, which produces sweat, which kindles fevers, which heals wounds? It is something in me, something extraordinary about me.

Linnæus burned with desire to get to know this extraordinary thing. From the impatient, vehement pulse of the very style one can see how strong this desire was. Linnæus's conception of the universe left no room for anything accidental, anything indifferent. A hasty and haughty utterance by an envious professor's wife he notes down immediately, and connects it with cases of disease and death. 'God sees and hears all,' he writes. 'Take care that Nemesis does not hear.'

Linnæus's belief in Nemesis can often take frightening and terrible forms; whether it can be factually justified or not is a question which cannot be proved one way or the other; it may be mentioned that an eminent Swedish writer at one time wrote a theoretically plausible refutation of Linnæus's Nemesis doctrine, only to give subsequently, in reaction to the pressure of world events, eloquent and moving expression day after day to a political Nemesis belief. Carl Linnæus's genius lay partly in the fact that he was passionately interested in facts. He could not conceive of anything factual being incidental, meaningless.

It has been pointed out in one edition of the Notes on *Nemesis Divina* that the Linnean form of retribution is practically always punitive, avenging, hardly ever rewarding or reparative. In the entire collection there is only one exception to this rule; nor is there any mention of equity, judgment, or compensation in another world. The only allusion in the Nemesis notes to what lies behind death's copper portal is suggestive more of Epicurus' doctrine than of Christianity: *Ede, bibe, lude; post mortem nulla voluptas.* (Eat, drink, and be merry; after death there is no pleasure.) It is, as appears from the subsequent references to the Bible, Epicurus' kindred spirit from the Old Testament, the author of Ecclesiastes, who is here the source of Linnæus's wisdom. The advice he gives his son is likewise mostly negative; he should be on his guard against Nemesis; he should avoid those sins whose punishment is demonstrated in the collection of examples; but he also is given two positive commandments: *Bene fac et lætare* (Do good and be merry). The words are to be found in Spinoza's *Ethica*.

One should not look for any philosophical consistency in Linnæus's attitude to Nemesis. It is not a ready-made mental edifice; it is only the material for one. At one moment he expresses an iron-hard determinism; at another he tries to reconcile his fatalism with his free will.

When reading these notes one is often reminded of Strindberg. But there is a distinct difference: Strindberg is nearly always occupied with his own right. In all his judicial expositions he appears personally as the plaintiff. But for Linnæus it was not a question of his own right. It was a question of universal, objective, and divine right. Strindberg wanted to show that he was in the right but had been proved wrong. Linnæus wanted to show that the evil which strikes us down is a just punishment. Fate is God's judgment, against which there is no appeal. *Fatum est judicium Dei contra quod nullum antifugium.* Not always, but now and then, this conviction approaches oriental fatalism. On page 32 it says: 'No evil befalls in the city but that the Lord does. Be it as it may, it is yet as God wills.' One is again reminded of *Politia Naturæ*.

Linnæus was religious inasmuch as he had a strong sense of what one might call a feeling of awe. When he chose *Numen adest* as his favourite words, he was being quite consistent. With his scientific rationalism, his need for systematism and his passion for theory he never refused to face the forbidden. A vein of primitivism runs through his way of thinking. This is revealed in the memoranda on *Nemesis Divina* not only when he speaks of portents and the resultant guises they assume, but also in expressions such as this (page 27):

Everyone becomes the unfortunate man's enemy. All shove the chariot of disaster along. Neither heaven nor earth can then help.

This, surely, should not be interpreted as a reflection on man's desire to cast himself *en masse* on anyone in distress, as Jaques in *As You Like It* philosophizes, but means, on the contrary, that an unfortunate man, according to Linnæus, is rightly shunned. For he is marked by God's finger.

The expanse of his spirit was wide and rich, and cannot be expressed in a single formula. His soul possessed breadth, depth, and intensity.

With his strange mixture of primitivism and rational scientific nature Linnæus was remarkably free from the prejudices of his age, from *idola fori*, the idols of the market-place, as the Bacon he admired would say. One can sense his democratism, unique for his time and class. The angle from which he regarded life made all men equal.

The Nemesis notes also contain the solution of his life's most thorny problem, that concerning his fortune, his burning desire for success and his fear of it. He ends by feeling giddy at the thought of his fortune. He exhorts his son never to seek fortune, but at the same time he can also gladly and humbly offer thanks for that which has been granted him. On the last page of the Nemesis notes is the following:

Thanks, Thou great, almighty God, for all the good Thou hast done me in this world.

CHAPTER XV

HAMMARBY

FROM Upsala to Hammarby is a moderately long walk, but the road is not as pretty or as varied as one might wish; it may even be asserted that the Upsala Plain, regarded as locality for walking, can well compete with the Plain of Lund in the matter of monotony and cheerlessness; this may be why our university people have been a somewhat sedentary race. And it is hard to imagine that this is really the classic ground of Swedish natural science, that it was really here, on these roads, that Linnæus made his excursions with pupils from Sweden and all the corners of Europe. The fauna and flora appear today to be almost equally poor. Flocks of crows flap across the fields, larks trill in the spring, in the winter one can follow the tracks of the fox as he hunts for food; this is about all. But it is important to bear in mind that the countryside between Upsala and Hammarby was rather different in Linnæus's time from what it is now. In his lectures on the animal kingdom Linnæus says of the little black tern (*Hydrochelidon nigra*; *Sterna nigra* with Linnæus), now one of our country's most rare birds, that it 'is to be found in abundance at Ultuna in the thick sedge growing in the lake and along by the shore'; the same statement occurs in his *Fauna Svecica*. Nowadays, this wonderfully pretty little bird is only to be found with us in one or two spots in Gotland and Öland, and in Skåne. The remark is of importance in this connection, as it shows what a different picture the landscape round Upsala presented in Linnæus's time. In those days the Upsala Plain consisted for the most part of low-lying fields with sedge and reed, rich in unusual plants and in the spring filled with the cry of waders and the bleat of wild ducks. Even during the latter half of the nineteenth century it was still a very profitable hunting-ground, at least during spring and autumn, and in one book of sporting memoirs there is an account of the spring-time flights of wild geese and swans and of the large flocks of pintails and golden-eyes on the flooded meadows.

All this has now gone; the earth is well drained; the little river, Sävjaån, meandering between the fields looks more like a ditch for the greater part of the year. This thorough drainage has of course been to the advantage not only of Uppland's agriculture but also the health of the people; in the old days miasmas rose from the marshy ground, and death from ague was very common in Upsala. Linnæus himself has written quite a lot about the Upsala ague and the method of combating it. Unfortunately, however, what is healthy does not always harmonize with what is beautiful, and when one walks across the plain below Hammarby in the fairest months of the year, one wonders if it did not gleam much more colourfully at the time when history's most renowned botanical excursions took place in this very spot. In ditch and pasture almost all one finds nowadays is dandelions. It is no longer the favourite haunt of Flora, sweet and fair.

How the Upsala Plain looked at harvest-time, when harvesting was in full swing, Linnæus has himself described at the end of his *Journey to Västergötland*. It is one of the most magnificent descriptions of the Swedish countryside we possess; it is, in fact, often quoted. Linnæus this time approached Upsala from the west, but his description applies equally well to the easterly part of the plain towards Danmark's church and Hammarby:

All the way from Fällingsbro the autumn has displayed itself before our eyes. The woods were still green; but graver than in the summer. Pasture and meadow were green, but without flowers, for the cattle had laid bare the former, and the scythe the latter. The fields were filled with golden stooks, and the yellowish stubble from the corn was interspersed with green weeds. The ditches were full of water, following on the wet summer, and the many marsh-marigolds made them yellow.

The wayside was covered with *Persicaria acri*, now beginning to turn red and hang its spikes.

Everywhere the countryman was outside hard at work: some of the peasants were reaping the corn with the sickle, while their womenfolk, whose heads and arms were quite white, bound it together, some were carting home their rye, some were threshing, some were harrowing the fields, some were sowing the winter rye, some were harrowing down the barley, some were levelling the field with the clod-crusher, while the herdsmen's children sang and blew their horns for the cattle that were grazing in the distant pastures, until the chill evening wind began to blow and the clear sun sink below the horizon, as we came into the garden at Upsala.

The master of Hammarby could gaze out across a Swedish Arcady as it lay there in its autumn splendour.

On towards Hammarby the woods obscure the view to the north, and the plains to the south open up towards the Mora Stones. Linnæus had very little feeling for historic atmosphere, and when in 1758 he became the owner of the manor of Hammarby, it is unlikely to have occurred to him as he stood at his garden gate that the countryside in front of him was the oldest and most illustrious in Sweden. For it was here that the Swedish kings were elected in pagan times.

At all events, we can feel justifiably pleased that Hammarby is situated in this particular neighbourhood. The property is very old, though its main building was not put up until Linnæus went to live there. It is first mentioned in a document as far back as 1337, when Olof Styrbjörnsson Gren acquired it from the Upsala canon, Lars Nilsson. It then passed through many hands until it was eventually bought by Linnæus, after whose death it was handed down in his family until his great-grandson, Carl Ridderbjelke, sold it to the Swedish State and the University of Upsala in 1879, since when Hammarby has been restored and cared for in a most exemplary way.

The Linnæus who lived at Hammarby during the summer has no place in the history of Swedish penury. He was royal physician and was soon to be ennobled. He was well supplied with this world's goods. Hammarby and Sävja he bought for 80,000 dalers, which was a lot of money at that time. The house was appointed in keeping with his position; it is now not so much the collections at Hammarby as those in the museum at the Linnæanum at Upsala which testify to the abundance of costly possessions: expensive china and glass-ware, gold snuff-boxes, a profusion of silver, rings and precious stones, costly silks and a comfortable supply of linen helped to make up the estate, whose greatest treasures, however, were the cabinet of natural-history specimens, the herbarium and the library. Linnæus, towards the end of his life, was a very well-to-do man.

That his life at Hammarby was also very happy has been vouched for chiefly by his descendant, Tycho Tullberg, whom we have to thank for our knowledge of many of the Linnean family traditions; but in all truth it cannot be said that the family life portrayed in the younger Linné's unpublished letters to Bäck after his father's death seems to have been harmonious. Tullberg writes: 'It is hardly likely that Linné, had he felt depressed and worried at home, would have possessed such gay spirits and such a sound outlook on life.' But the ageing Linnæus often shows in his letters a heavy and melancholy frame of mind, and his notes on *Nemesis Divina* speak of a dark outlook on life. It is also known that the man who was worn out and broken in mind and body was forced by his wife right up to the last to go on with the academic recording work he considered so pointless in order to increase the family's wealth. And his final expedition — when he got the farm-hand to drive him out one dark winter's night to the empty house at Sävja, where he lay down in front of the fire with his pipe — is all too suggestive of flight.

But it is not so much his family life one thinks of when walking through the garden and park at Hammarby on a June day. The garden in front of the main building is quite wonderful in the month of flowers. Moses' burning bush shines in peculiar splendour; *Dictamnus* is its Latin name, and Linnæus has mentioned it in several places, amongst others in

Hortus Upsaliensis; and the scent of the low-clipped box-hedge is strong and inciting. According to Tullberg this part of the grounds was an orchard during the eighteenth century; the real garden is supposed to have lain to the east of the main building, where plants now grow wild in a snaring tangle beneath the spreading trees.

Today the vegetation is much more luxuriant than in Linnæus's time. 'Out of the very abode of death', Linnæus called out to his wife: 'Look after my grove that I have planted while you live, and if trees die out, set others in their stead.' There are not many places where the leafy trees flourish better than on the knoll behind Hammarby. It is as it should be that the vegetation is allowed to grow wild. Columbines, blue and pink, are in flower everywhere in the middle of June among the wild chervil. It is probable that they were introduced by Linnæus himself; at all events it is certain (according to Tullberg at least) that the large, handsome edible snails (*Helix pomatia*) that now creep about in large numbers on the moss-clad boulders are a Linnean import. The trees were not as numerous or as leafy 150 years ago. Linnæus used to hang glass bells on them and listen to the tinkling as the wind stirred in the tree-tops.

One likes to imagine how this glass harmonica must have sounded in the elms and limes of Hammarby. But on a morning in June a glass harmonica is superfluous; another harmony is heard from the trees. Seldom have I heard louder bird-song. It was not so pure as it can be in May; the cheeping and chirruping of newly-hatched fledglings formed a constant and unmusical background; hundreds of baby starlings were particularly energetic in their impatient demands on their parents. But the thrush was still singing, the garden warbler, the willow warbler, and the white-throat could be heard, the pied flycatcher was twittering, the chaffinch warbled, the cuckoo and the green woodpecker called, and one or two deeper notes, faintly discernible in the powerful orchestra, seemed to indicate that the icterine warbler had also taken up its abode at Hammarby.

All-obliterating Time can now and then be strangely merciful. National cultures germinate, flower and wither like grass. There is nothing permanent under the crescent moon. Even in this park, so carefully tended by gentle hands to the memory of a great man, it must be said that in 150 years everything visible has changed so much that one cannot be sure whether a single one of its living trees was ever touched by Linnæus's hand.

But something else is left in the park at Hammarby, which it is difficult to express in words. The vegetation's almost tropical profusion on a Swedish June day and the unceasing chorus of birds accentuate the historical memories of the place in a very moving way. The somewhat dry plain spreads out in front; the fir woods behind stand silent and bare; but among these grey rocks the eye is dazzled by flowers, the ear is filled with bird-song, and one is intoxicated by the scent.

Chronos, the god of time, has dealt harshly with the Mora Stones, but he has had a seemly respect for Linnæus.

*　　　*　　　*

Two of Linnæus's foreign pupils have fully and picturesquely described everyday life at Hammarby. One is Fabricius, the Danish entomologist, also known as a pre-Darwinist. He tells us:

For two whole years, i.e. from 1762 to '64, I had the privilege of enjoying his instruction, his guidance, his intimate company. Not a day passed but I did not meet him, partly attending his lectures, and also frequently spending several hours with him in amiable conversation. In the summer we went with him out to the country. There were then three of us there who were foreigners: Kuhn, Zoëga and I. In the wintertime we had our dwelling directly opposite to his, and thither he would come almost every day in his short red dressing-gown and a green fur cap, with a pipe in his hand. He would come for half-an-hour and remain for a whole hour, many a time for two. His conversation meanwhile was extremely cheerful and agreeable. Either it took the form of anecdotes about men learned in his science, whom he had got to know within or without his native land, or else it enlightened our doubt and our knowledge in general. While talking he would laugh to his heart's content and his face would light up with a joy and gaiety which clearly showed how disposed his mind was to the familiarities of social intercourse.

Even happier was our life in the country. We lived some few furlongs from his dwelling at Hammarby in a thatched cottage where we had arranged ourselves after our own discretion and kept our own household. He used to get up very early in the summertime, usually about 4 o'clock. About 6 he would come to us, as the building of his dwelling-house was not yet completed, share breakfast with us and lecture on *Ordines naturales plantarum* for as long as it pleased him, usually it was getting on for 10. Then, until about 12 o'clock, we would walk round on the nearby rocks, which kept us sufficiently occupied by reason of what was growing there. In the afternoon we would visit him in his garden, and in the evening we used to play trisett with his wife.

On Sundays the whole family was for the most part with us, and then we would occasionally summon a peasant with a musical instrument which looked like a violin, and we would dance in the barn belonging to the farm with the greatest jollity. To be sure, our balls were not particularly dazzling, the company not numerous, the music beneath all criticism, the dances of very limited variety — minuet and polka, but nevertheless we greatly enjoyed ourselves. The old man would spend the time smoking a pipe with Zoega, looking on, and dancing too for that matter, but only seldom, and then only the polka, in which he excelled all us younger ones. He liked to see us merry the while, even noisy; otherwise he feared that we were not content.

This is how Fabricius describes Linnæus's appearance:

Carl von Linné was of small stature, and as he had a slight stoop he appeared even smaller than he really was. He was otherwise powerfully built, but lean, and when I knew him advancing age had already furrowed his brow with wrinkles. His face was ingenuous, nearly always gay, and greatly resembled the portrait in *Species Plantarum*. His eyes were the most beautiful I have ever seen. They were anything but large, it is true, but they had a lustre and a penetrating quality that I have never seen in anyone else's. To be sure, I cannot recall their colour, but I was often given a look which seemed to pierce right into my very soul.

Linnæus's eyes were brown.—Fabricius goes on to speak of his delightful disposition, of his ambition, which only concerned his scientific fame but within this limitation was very strong, of his thrift and of his happiness. Of Mrs. Sara Linnæus he writes that 'she was tall, strong, domineering, selfish, and ill-bred'. That she hated her son to such an extent that 'in the whole wide world he had no more bitter enemy than his mother', sounds an exaggeration, but would seem unfortunately to be confirmed by the scenes in the home after his father's decease. Fabricius writes of Linné the younger that he was of course not comparable with his father, but that his great knowledge and familiarity with his father's scientific writings would at all events be sure to make him a competent academic teacher. Of the girls he writes that they were 'raw children of nature', and although this may be so, there is yet a letter amongst the Thunberg collection in the university library at Upsala from one of the von Linné girls which, in the matters of the writing, style, and spelling of the Swedish and French languages, is most excellently written.

Another foreigner who was very familiar with the Linnean home life was the German, Johann Beckmann, who in his book *Schwedische Reise* 1765-1766 has quite a lot to relate both from Hammarby and Linnæus's house in Upsala. His description of his first meeting with Linnæus is very vivid. Beckmann had arrived in Upsala on September 6th, and in those days, as now, the old university town had rather an empty look before term began. The great man was living at Hammarby for the summer, and Beckmann had written to him earlier in the year from St. Petersburg.

I went, however, into a bookshop and found there a man somewhat up in years, not very tall, with dusty shoes and hose, a very unshaven chin, and an old green coat, on which a decoration was hanging. I was not a little amazed when I was told that this was the renowned Linnæus. I addressed him as he made to go, and that in Latin, as he did not entirely understand German. He immediately recalled my letter and was prodigiously polite.

In October Beckmann went out to Hammarby.

I was received by him in the most friendly way, and he pressed me to stay the night, which, however, I was unable to do because of the hired coach. On this estate, to which belonged several adjacent farms, the walls of his rooms were so thickly pasted with engravings of plants from the most costly books by Sloane and Ehret etc., that they appeared to be papered. — Mrs. von Linné is the daughter of the late Dr. Moræus of Falun, and is not so courteous to strangers as her husband. Her altogether too bourgeois manner of dressing does not induce respect.

And then follows a rather pointless description of an altercation with the lady in question.

He often went to Hammarby subsequently, and became very interested in the Mora Stones. He also tells how at this time the interest in natural science, which had flourished so well in Upsala during the '40s, was now in the process of decline.

Love of natural history has, even in Sweden, almost died out, so that appart from Linnæus, father and son, there are not 4 people who take pains to study it with due seriousness. Nor in Upsala does one have nearly so many opportunities for it as foreigners suppose. Above all it is difficult to acquire there even the most fundamental knowledge, as the professor is not accustomed to giving systematic instruction and busying himself with trifles, but prefers his listeners to discuss the subject with him and ask him questions concerning what they do not rightly grasp.

This is an exaggeration; natural-scientific research in Sweden still had many illustrious names, but compared with the '40s it was undoubtedly on the wane. Beckmann goes on to say that the other professors regarded with ill-concealed envy the flocking of foreigners round Linnæus's chair; nor did Linnæus for his part care to see strangers attending other lectures than his own.

All this cast a shadow. The Hammarby family was not popular in university circles. Its very position, rank, and affluence debarred it from that.

*　　*　　*

During the 1770s Carl von Linné — for that is what we must now call him — was often very ill. In his speech on the delights of nature, *Deliciæ Naturæ*, which he delivered on the occasion of his retiring from the post of Rector of the University in December 1772, he referred to his infirmity in a brilliant turn of phrase:

But this cold season, this cold cathedral, my cold years and your patience, gentlemen, which is beginning to cool, command me to desist.

Yes, the cold years were beginning. He felt worn out. Nearly all his organs were giving him trouble and his whole body ached. In May 1774 he had a stroke. It became increasingly difficult for him to write, his memory failed, his speech was muddled and his mind began to wander. Bright intervals occurred, but during 1776 he grew steadily worse.

An infinitely moving document is his last letter to his friend Bäck. It is dated December 1756; but Linné wrote 1756 in mistake for 1776. He had just received a letter from Bäck in which the latter referred to the recent death of his seventeen-year-old son who had showed such promise: 'God has resolved otherwise and it has been His wish to lose more than half of the bonds which hold me to this earth'.

It is these words which the sick Linné has in mind when he tries laboriously to form one or two sentences. He wants to express his sympathy, but the words elude him. Even so one senses behind the vague and ill-defined phrases a kindly will groping its way along. This is how the great Swedish genius now wrote:

Nuper Diear Brother.
as greatly as I have triied to rejoice in a a in a frend so gratly must I trouble him now.
God haas resolved to loos more than hafl of of the bebonds which have held me to thiss earth.

Vale, to loos; only way out, that way out may ba loost.
Farewehl. I am Brother's; Brother is mine.
I am my My Brother's Constant Brother faithful to death
Linné.

It is tragic. It is horrible. But even in the tragicality there
is a glimmer of sunlight. The spheres were darkening. From
1777 there is this description of his illness:

All his limbs and organs, particularly the tongue, the lower
extremities and the bladder, were paralysed. His speech was
incoherent and very often unintelligible. He could not move
from the spot where he was sitting or lying without the help of
others, nor could he undress himself, eat, or perform the least
thing he required. Of his organic life only the breath,
digestion, and circulation of the blood were still in tolerably
good condition. Everything else was more or less destroyed.
He had even forgotten his own name, and he seemed for the
most part to be without consciousness of past or present.

But this description is not quite complete. Sparrman says
of his great teacher in the month of May from Hammarby:

Allows himself sometimes to be led down into the garden,
delights in the plants, but no longer knows them.

He had become a child again. But he also had the child's
joy. He was again at Stenbrohult. He delighted in the plants,
whose names he did not know. Knowledge had gone. Wonder
remained.

Occasionally his mind would brighten for a moment. This
would happen, it is told, 'when he found lying in front of him
one or two books dealing with botany or zoology, including his
own, which he would dip into with visible pleasure and let it
be understood that he would have considered himself happy if
he could have been the author of such useful works'.

Even when confronted with his own achievements he was
capable of the child's wonder.

His was the heritage in full measure that Gilbert Keith
Chesterton has described in a poem called 'A Second Childhood':

Men grow too old for love, my love,
men grow too old for wine,
but I shall not grow too old to see
unearthly daylight shine,
changing my chamber's dust to snow
till I doubt if it be mine.

Behold, the crowning mercies melt,
the first surprises stay;
and in my dross is dropped a gift
for which I dare not pray:
that a man grow used to grief and joy
but not to night and day.

*   *   *

A thrill of thunder in my hair:
though blackening clouds be plain,
still I am stung and startled
by the first drops of the rain:
romance and pride and passion pass
and these are what remain.

Strange crawling carpets of the grass,
wide windows of the sky:
so in this perilous grace of God
with all my sins go I:
and things grow new though I grow old,
though I grow old and die.

Carl von Linné, so highly gifted and favoured by the gods, was deprived of everything before he died, except one thing — *curiositas naturalis.*

★   ★   ★

In his son's letters to Bäck there are one or two details about Carl von Linné's last illness and death which may be worth quoting. In an undated letter (clearly from 1777) Linné the younger says that his father was still strong enough to take pleasure in 'the advancement which botany has gained of late through the potentates'. But on December 30th, 1777, he says hopelessly:

This time my father has had the most frightful attack of convulsions in his face and down his whole body, so that I feared each breath would be the last; left alone with him; for no *medici* were in town; now this has again been overcome, but God knows for how long.

In the next letter, dated January 4th, 1778, he says that his father's 'most grievous pain is now *pyuria Vesicæ*'.

On January 10th came the end. The only ones present at his death-bed were Sam. Duse, engaged to the family's youngest daughter, and an English pupil, John Rotheram. The following day, 11th, Linné the younger writes to Bäck: 'On 10th Jan. at 2 o'clock my dear Father died. In my opinion *Pyuria Vesicæ* was the cause of his death, to which his weakness contributed.' In modern medical language, therefore, if the son is right, the immediate cause of Linné's death seems to have been hypertrophy of the prostate.

There was no peaceful atmosphere in the house of mourning. As early as January 16th Linné the younger complains — justly, one thinks — regarding the ostentatious form of the obituary notice: 'The obstinacy of the women and the many advisers in the house of mourning insisted that this be printed exactly as it had been drawn up.' Then followed a quarrel about the deceased's estate. On February 12th Linné the younger writes:

I still do not know whether my father's herbarium will come to me in accordance with his disposition, but surely the library and all the rest of his collections will do so; were my mother and sisters more reasonable towards me, more justly minded, I ought to have some hopes of getting it, even if it were not so ordered in the disposition. It would be of great help to me, and also mean the preservation of my late Father's reputation (which might otherwise suffer greatly in the hands of those with the desire to criticize him), but it is difficult for me to make them see this; my desire not to show an unseemly interest, and the conviction that expostulation by me would not be taken in the right way, restrains me.

The quarrel seems to have increased in volume and intensity. On February 20th he says: 'My co-heirs are alway trying to prevent me from getting anywhere, and are always suspicious the moment anything is requested by me.' Gradually, however, the younger Linné seems to have become more sure of himself; when on July 21st he writes of 'Banks' cruel offer' (i.e. the first English feelers concerning the purchase of the herbarium) he is able to add stoutly: 'No one filches from me a single plant.'

One gets the impression, however, when reading the younger Linné's letters, that he was thinking not so much of personal advantage as the care of his father's memory, and one also feels that the young man, so roundly hated by all the grumblers at the Upsala university, really possessed both feeling for his great inheritance and the ability to look after it. In an undated letter from 1778 he has most excellently characterized his father's genius as a botanist. He writes:

My late Father's secret in determining *genera*, so that species did not become new *genera*? Was none other than knowing the plants *ab externa facie* (by their outward appearance). In that respect he often deviated from his own system. Variation *in numero partium* did not disturb him so long as the *caracter generis* was still preserved. This is not the practice of others abroad who, whenever they find a cellular structure new to them, immediately create another *genus*; in this way *genera* are becoming overwhelmingly numerous.

Linné's genius as a botanical systematist has to my knowledge never been better or more clearly expressed. And the son's proud loyalty to his father's memory and achievements is apparent in a letter to Bäck from 1781, occasioned by 'a crowd of new botanical scribes who zealously try to lead science into confusion'. It is the legitimate heir-apparent's wrath flashing in these words:

All seem to feel that they have the right to create new *genera* and species, even although they are incapable of rightly describing a plant or animal. There have recently been shameless passages in the proceedings of both Lund and Göteborg Societies of Science which evidence the decline of natural science here, its former home.

Science is perhaps not in the long run served by such a strong piety, such a passionate orthodoxy. But it shows in what relationship the likeable and gifted Linné the younger stood to the father whose shadow too, no doubt, must occasionally have inspired him with awe. We shall leave him there.

*　　*　　*

When Linné the younger died it required a great deal of work at Hammarby to pack and nail up the packing-cases in which the Linnean relics were dispatched lock, stock, and barrel to England. That the Hon. Mrs. von Linné should have known much about manuscripts is asking too much, and let us not grieve over what happened. The English have cared for the treasures better than we Swedes would have done.

In his last days the old master of Hammarby was no more affected by earthly happenings. One imagines that he finally left his grove and the memory of it with the same hope that his pupil Fabricius once expressed in these lines regarding what can be expected to lie behind the temple doors of death:

Memory of the time lived here on this earth is hardly likely. We know nothing of the time of our birth, and the memory of bygone times is utterly quenched in an old person. This much seems to me probable, through the observance of nature, that the spirit which lives within me is separated from the body and is not destroyed simultaneously with it. My Creator's goodness, which is so conspicuous everywhere in nature, is a surety to me that the condition of the soul after death, however it may be, is not worse than here on earth. I therefore await even death with calm and confidence and presume that in the hereafter also I shall continue the observance of nature with greater knowledge and greater confidence.

So Linnæus may have thought. So he should have thought. If he did so, and if in that case he was right, then *curiositas naturalis*, even on the other side of the frontier of the Unknown, must be the only lasting thing.

Linnæus took a dark view of human life, and never tried to gild reality. He was able nevertheless to give praise and thanks. He was a valiant man. We need him.

LINNÆUS AND ENGLAND

AT the end of *De Profundis* Oscar Wilde says:

Linnæus fell on his knees and wept for joy when he saw for the first time the long heath of some English upland made yellow with the tawny aromatic blossoms of the common furze; and I know that for me, to whom flowers are part of desire, there are tears waiting in the petals of some rose.

Wilde no doubt had in mind what Sir J. E. Smith, the founder of the Linnean Society, wrote in Rees's *The New Cyclopaedia XXI* many years before Wilde was born: 'Linnæus was so enchanted with the gorse in full flower on Putney Heath, that he flung himself on his knees before it.' The story is probably made up, as it was not in Linnæus's nature to behave so theatrically, but it shows the strength of the Linnean tradition in England; and the very fact that the broken man in Reading Gaol let his imagination dwell on Linnæus as he sat and dreamt of freedom, says a great deal for the Swedish scientist's hold on people's minds.

In 1933 a large volume was published with the title *A Catalogue of the Works of Linnæus (and Publications more immediately relating thereto) preserved in the Libraries of the British Museum (Bloomsbury) and the British Museum (Natural History) (South Kensington).* It is what one may call a commentated bibliography, containing about 4000 headings, and is a magnificent work. Its editor, B. H. Soulsby, was Assistant Keeper in charge of the Library of the British Museum, and he died shortly before this great work was completed. It is the largest bibliographical tribute ever paid to a Swedish author. The fact that it was produced in England was not mere chance.

The books about Linnæus are now so comprehensive that no one man can master them in detail. In England today it is really only the learned experts for whom Linnæus is a living name, but it was not always so. In 1799 a small book with delightful coloured plates was published in London. It bears the title *Thirty-eight Plates with Explanations intended to illustrate Linnæus's System of Vegetables*. The author was Thomas Martyn, Regius Professor of Botany in the University of Cambridge. In spite of the author's position as a man of science, the book was intended for popular use. In simple words and with beautiful pictures the book illustrates the Linnean sexual system in the clearest possible manner. One likes to imagine one of Jane Austen's heroines sitting with the book in her lap, idly turning the leaves. The great interest in flowers, so characteristic of England of the eighteenth and nineteenth centuries, undoubtedly had its origin in books such as this.

It would be wrong to think, however, that Linnæus had inspired the same interest in nature study in England as he had done in Sweden. In England the passion for animals and flowers had ancient roots. It may be worth quoting what a long-since-forgotten author by the name of Daniel C. Carr wrote concerning this in a little book, published anonymously in London in 1844, called *Linnæus and Jussieu; or the Rise and Progress of Systematic Botany*:

In our own country witchcraft and the knowledge of herbs were for a long time associated together, and advantage was taken of this circumstance by Shakespeare, in his description of incantations, where he fails not to introduce 'root of hemlock', 'slips of yew', &c. In the reign of Henry the Eighth, the cultivation of medicinal herbs began to occupy the attention of surgeons and apothecaries; private herb gardens were planted, and Gerard, called the 'Father of English herbalists', possessed the principal one.

By referring to the works of that excellent man, George Herbert, whose writings are full of originality and beauty, we find the knowledge of herbs to have been considered indispensably requisite to a country clergyman. Herbert wrote his *Priest to the Temple* about the year 1630, and in the admirable rules which he has laid down for the regulation of the pastors' conduct, he especially enforces the duty of attending his flock in sickness, and of being himself, as far as it is safe and desirable, their physician. He recommends the study of anatomy and physic, and the use of a herbal. He says that the reading of such subjects and the knowing of herbs 'may be done at such times as they may be a help and a recreation to more divine studies, as also by way of illustration, even as our Saviour made plants and seeds to teach the people; for he was the true householder, who bringeth out of his treasure things new and old; the old things of philosophy, and the new of grace; and maketh the one serve the other. In the knowledge of simples, wherein the manifold wisdom of God is wonderfully to be seen, one thing would be carefully observed; which is, to know what herbs may be used instead of drugs of the same nature, and to make the garden the shop; for home-bred medicines are both more easy for the parson's purse, and more familiar for all men's bodies. So where the apothecary useth rhubarb or bolearmena, the parson useth damask or white roses, plantain, shepherd's purse, and knot-grass, with better success. As for spices, he doth not only prefer home-bred things before them, but condemns them for vanities, and so shuts them out of his family, esteeming that there is no spice comparable, for herbs, to rosemary, thyme, savoury, and mints; and for seeds, to fennel and caraway seeds. Accordingly, for salves, his wife seeks not the city, but prefers her garden and fields before all outlandish gums. And surely hyssop, valerian, mercury, adder's tongue, yerrow, melilot, and St. John's-wort, made into a salve, and elder, camomile, mallows, comphrey, and smallage, made into a poultice, have done great and rare cures'.

We do not find any mention of a public herb-garden in England previous to the planting of one at Oxford, called by a writer of that day 'a spacious, illustrious physicke-garden, beautifully walled and gated'; which took place about the year 1640. Forty-five years later the Chelsea gardens were in a flourishing state, and artificial heat was used in green-houses, which seems, by Evelyn's manner of speaking of it, to have been then a new introduction. The notice in his *Diary* is as follows:

'I went to see Mr. Wats, keeper of the Apothecaries' Garden of Simples at Chelsea, where there is a collection of innumerable rarities of that sort, particularly, besides rare annuals, the tree bearing Jesuits' bark, which has done such wonders in quartan agues. What was very ingenious, was the subterranean heate, conveyed by a stove under the conservatory, all vaulted with brick, so as he has the doores and windowes open in the hardest frost, secluding only the snow.'

Both at the gardens of Chelsea and Kew, there are at present very superb collections of plants, and the advance in horticultural knowledge has been exceedingly rapid throughout our country. The simple herbs which find a place alike in splendid botanical gardens and in the little plat of ground allotted to the humble cottager, have many of them received most appropriate and significant names in times past, by which they are still recognized among the lower class of people. The following amusing extract from the *Journal of a Naturalist,* will give a pretty good notion of the old-fashioned plan of naming herbs and plants:

'In ages of simplicity, when every man was the usual dispenser of good or bad, benefit or injury, to his own household or his cattle, — ere the veterinary art was known, or the drugs of other regions introduced, — necessity looked up to the products of its own clime, and the real or fantastical virtues of them were called to the trial, and thus was manifested the reasonableness of bestowing upon plants and herbs such names as might immediately indicate their several uses, or fitness for application; when distinctive characters, had they been given, would have been little attended to; and hence the numbers found favourable to the cure of particular complaints, the ailments of domestic creatures, or deemed injurious to them. Modern science may wrap up the meaning of its epithets in Greek or Latin terms: but in very many cases they are the mere translation of these despised "old vulgar names". What pleasure it must have afforded the poor sufferer in body or in limb— what confidence he must have felt of relief, when he knew that the good neighbour who came to bathe his wounds, or assuage his inward torments, brought with him such things as "all-heal, bruise-wort, gout-weed, fever-few" (fugio) and twenty other such comfortable mitigators of his afflictions; why their very names would almost charm away the sense of pain! The modern recipe contains no such terms of comfortable assurance: its meanings are all dark to the sufferer; its influence unknown. And then the good herbalists of old professed to have plants which were "all-good"; they could assuage anger by their "loose-strife"; they had "honesty true-love, and heart's-ease". The cayennes, the soys, the ketchups, and extra-tropical condiments of these days were not required, when the next thicket would produce "poor man's pepper, sauce-alone, and hedge-mustard"; and the woods and wilds around, when they yielded such delicate viands as "fat-hen, lambs-quarters, way-bread, butter, and eggs, with codlins and cream", afforded no despicable bill of fare. No one ever yet thought of accusing our old simplers of avarice, or love of lucre, yet their "thrift" is always to be seen; we have their humble "penny-wort, herb-two-pence, money-wort, silver-weed, and gold". We may smile, perhaps, at the cognomens or commemorations of friendship or worth recorded by the old simplers — at the herbs "Bennet, Robert, Christopher, Gerard, or Basil"; but do the names so bestowed by modern science read better, or sound better? it has "Lightfootia, Lapeyrousia, Hedwigia, Schkuhria, Scheuch-zeria"; and surely we may admit, in common benevolence, such partialities as "Good King Henry, Sweet William, Sweet Marjory, Sweet Cicely, Lettuce, Mary-gold, and Rose". These are epithets however so very extraordinary that we must consider them as mere perversions, or at least incapable of explanation at this period. The terms of modern science waver daily; names undergo an annual change, fade with the leaf, and give place to others; but the ancient terms, which some may ridicule, have remained for centuries, and will yet remain till nature is swallowed up by art. No; let our ancient herbal-ists, "a grave and whiskered race", retain the honours due to their labours, which were more needful and important ones at those periods: by them were many casualties and sufferings of man and beast relieved; and by aid of perseverance, better constitutions to act upon, and faith to operate, than we possess, they probably effected cures, which we moderns should fail to accomplish if attempted.'

In a somewhat droll — one is tempted to say Linnean or artful — manner, this same Carr has also given an important account of Linnæus's great English precursor, John Ray:

Numerous additions were made to the existing knowledge of plants by travellers in the new world. Public botanical gardens became general; but systematic botany did not advance until after the restoration of the Stuarts to the throne of England, and the termination of the long and bloody wars which distracted Europe. The influence of peace upon the progress of science was very great: systematic arrangements of plants appeared in great numbers, among which must be noticed the work of Robert Morison, a Scotchman, who was wounded fighting on the royalist side, in the civil wars of England. On the triumph of the republicans, he withdrew to France, and became director of the garden of Gaston, duke of Orléans, at Blois; where he was noticed by Charles II; who, on his restoration, invited Morison to England. He became superintendent of the royal gardens, and also of the botanic garden at Oxford. His great systematic work appeared at Oxford in 1680; but in the construction of it he appears to have borrowed largely from Cæsalpinus.

Among those whose efforts had the greatest and earliest influence in the construction of a vegetable system, was John Ray, or Wray, fellow of Trinity College, Cambridge, at the same time with Newton. He was the son of a blacksmith, at Black Notley, near Braintree, in Essex. He was born Nov. 29, 1628, educated at Braintree school, and sent thence to Catharine Hall, Cambridge, from whence he removed, after two years, to Trinity College. His progress in classical acquirements was so great, that the learned Duport, his tutor, spoke of Ray, and his friend Isaac Barrow, as the chief of all his pupils, to whom none of the rest were comparable. Nor was he deficient in mathematical knowledge, as his honours prove. He obtained a fellowship, and was chosen, in 1651, Greek lecturer of the College; in 1653, mathematical lecturer; in 1655, humanity reader; and, in successive years, other important offices were conferred upon him.

Ray acquitted himself honourably, both as a tutor and preacher (for college preaching at that period was frequently performed by persons not ordained), and was celebrated for the solid and useful divinity contained in his sermons. His favourite study, to which he contrived to devote a large portion of time in spite of his numerous duties, was natural history. He published in 1660 a *Catalogue of Cambridge Plants*, in order to promote the study of botany, which was then greatly overlooked. This work was so favourably received that he was encouraged to extend his researches through the greatest part of England, Wales, and Scotland. At the restoration of the king, Ray entered into holy orders, and was ordained by Sanderson, bishop of Lincoln. He continued fellow of Trinity College until the Bartholomew act required a subscription against the solemn league and covenant, when he resigned his fellowship rather than sign that declaration.

In 1663 Ray in company with three friends visited divers parts of Europe, and subsequently published the *Observations* made in that tour. He became a fellow of the Royal Society in 1667, and in 1669, he, with his friend Mr. Willoughby, made those experiments and observations on the rising and falling of the sap in trees, which are published in the Philosophical Transactions. His *Catalogue of English Plants* came out in 1670, of which he speaks with characteristic humility.

In June 1673, Ray married the daughter of Mr. Oakeley, of Launton in Oxfordshire, the lady being his junior by about twenty-four years. The writings of Ray were extremely numerous, and prove the indefatigable nature of his studies. Collections of proverbs and of unusual and local words were his lighter productions, while he also brought out in 1682 his *Methodus Plantarum Nova*, and in 1686 and 7 his *Historia Plantarum*, a vast and critical compilation. A supplement to this work appeared in 1704. But he also published other botanical works at this period, of which his Synopsis is declared to be alone sufficient to establish his fame.

In 1691 he published a work which has formed the basis of the labours of many following divines. It was called *The Wisdom of God manifested in the Works of the Creation*. Other theological pieces followed: and afterwards he wrote on quadrupeds, birds, and fishes. But increasing infirmities began to limit his writings; and in September 1698, he declared, in a letter to a friend, that he was unable so much as to walk into the neighbouring fields. Yet he continued many of his favourite studies, and especially devoted himself to that of insects. 'This great and wise man', says his biographer, 'in the full possession of his powers, and in the anticipation of the most glorious manifestations of his Creator, did not disdain or neglect to contemplate him in his least and lowest works'. Ray died in his house at Black Notley, January 17th, 1705, in the seventy-seventh years of his age. Derham says of him, that he was devout towards God; compassionate and charitable towards his fellow-creatures; just in his dealings; humble, courteous and affable in his conversation.

The plan of arranging plants adopted by this distinguished man consists of thirty-five classes, formed according to the habit and external appearance of the plants; their greater or less degree of perfection; their place of growth; the number of seeds, fruits, petals, or sepals to each flower; the nature of the fruit, or inflorescence. His method in many respects approximated to a natural one; and Sir J. E. Smith considered that Ray, as a botanist, was eclipsed by few but Linnæus.

In a country with such botanical and zoological traditions as England, Linné's revolutionary reforms were not, naturally enough, received with rapture at the outset. As late as the year before Linné's death — 1777, that is — Gilbert White wrote to his learned brother the Rev. John White, that the latter should refer in his works to the Linnean nomenclature, 'because though it is the fashion now to despise Linn. yet many languish privately to understand his method'. And the author of the great biography of Gilbert White, Rashleigh Holt-White, sums up by saying: 'The Linnean method was for many years unpopular in this country.' But Gilbert White himself greatly admired Linnæus; in 1770 he writes to his brother John: 'I am glad to find you begin to relish Linn: there is nothing to be done in the wide boundless field of natural history without a system.' But the books by Linnæus which were known, read and respected in England, were of course only the great technical Latin works; people were unaware that the Swedish natural scientist was also a great writer.

There came a change, however. After his death Linnæus became an English citizen. In other words: his collections and manuscripts were removed to London, and the society which has done most to preserve his memory is the Linnean Society of London.

A Swedish scientist and librarian, Dr. Arvid Uggla, has described the Linnean Society's origin and development:

When Carl von Linné's active life drew to a close on 10th January, 1778, it was found from his will that his scientific collections were to be handed down in the family in the same way as the rest of his estate. As his widow, Sara Lisa Moraea, at this period showed an increasingly marked financial aptitude — she had three unmarried daughters to provide with a dowry — the collections were even then in danger of being sold to a foreign buyer and taken out of the country. The younger Linné, however, for whose lectures they were practically indispensable, managed with the help of the executors of the estate to come to an arrangement whereby he received his father's herbarium and other collections by renouncing his share in the landed property.

Even as early as this, however, a prospective buyer had appeared — the wealthy English natural historian, collector, and explorer, Sir Joseph Banks. 'Banks's cruel offer', as Linné the younger described it to a friend, was declined. The years 1781-83 Linné the younger spent travelling abroad in order to fit himself for the chair he had originally received as a reward to his father for the latter's services. The greater part of this time he spent in England, where he was received with the utmost politeness and good-will (not least by the aforementioned Banks) and made particularly valuable scientific contacts.

About six months after his return home, however, Linné the younger died, on 1st November, 1783, and the male line thereby became extinct. The matter of the estate immediately arose. The mother and sisters were the sole heirs, and the father's collections and library were the most valuable part of it. A friend of the family, J. G. Acrel, who was executor, was asked by Mrs. von Linné to try and sell them for the highest possible price, and Acrel immediately got in touch with Banks.

EPILOGUE

But in the meantime Banks had increased his own scientific collections to such an extent — they are now preserved in the British Museum — that he now saw no reason for acquiring the Linnean ones.

As chance would have it, however, Banks happened to be breakfasting with one or two other scientists when he received word that Linné's collections were now for sale for a given price of 1,000 guineas. One of those present was a twenty-four-year-old medical student, James Edward Smith, the son of a prosperous manufacturer in Norwich. He had already shown great interest in and knowledge of botany, and Banks now suggested that he try and make himself owner of Linné's famous herbarium. Smith was keenly interested, and immediately wrote to Acrel declaring himself willing to offer the stated sum provided that the further particulars he asked for came up to his expectations. He then wrote to his father who, with his shrewd business sense, expressed a doubt that these collections would be permitted to leave Sweden 'for such a paltry penny', when Linné's famous book collection alone was worth the money. And yet this is what actually happened!

For some unaccountable reason, no one in Sweden was sufficiently interested to make a bid for the collections, and Smith energetically pushed forward the negotiations. The catalogue he received on request from Acrel showed that the purchase covered far more than he could possibly have conceived at the outset. There were about 19,000 plant-sheets, 3,200 insects, 1,500 shells, 7-800 corals, 2,500 kinds of stones and minerals. To this was added Linné's great natural scientific library comprising about 2,500 volumes. On receiving this information Smith was not slow to clench the deal, and on 25th June Acrel received word that half the purchase price had already been deposited with a merchant in Amsterdam to the credit of the vendors. Acrel immediately set about having the collections packed up, and at the end of September they left Stockholm in an English ship.

The collections, packed in 26 large chests, arrived in London at the end of October 1784. It is easy to imagine the excitement and joy with which the young buyer unpacked them. Over and above what has already been mentioned, there was also a collection of manuscripts, not only from the hand of Linné, father and son, but also those that had been sent by other contemporary scientists. And last, but not least, there was Linné's entire correspondence, so important from a scientific point of view, of about 3,000 letters from a large number of correspondents. It may be wondered whether the young Smith was at that time fully aware of the position which the possession of all these treasures would give him within the world of science. It must be remembered that for decades Linnæus had been practically the absolute dictator in the botanical world, without whose approval a new plant-name could scarcely be introduced. And here were *his own* specimens, those on which he had built his descriptions in the editions (by degrees enlarged) of *Species Plantarum* and *Systema Naturæ*, in other words what we now call the original specimens. Whoever possessed this treasure must gradually come to occupy a central position in natural science, as every botanist who wanted to identify a plant species beyond all doubt had Linné's own specimen to compare it with.

Smith went abroad for two years to complete his medical studies, and on arriving home in the autumn of 1787 he got in touch with a number of influential men interested in natural science (among them Sir Joseph Banks, then president of the Royal Society, and Mr. — afterwards Bishop — S. Goodenough) and together with them formed the Linnean Society in the spring of 1788. Smith, although the youngest of the members, was elected president of the new society, a post which he held until his death in 1828. He devoted himself almost entirely to botany and the care of his newly-acquired collections, and it must be readily admitted that he proved himself fully worthy to administer these treasures by his willingness to place them at the disposal of the scientific world and by his efforts in every possible way to make Linné's writings known. He carried on an extensive correspondence with naturalists all over the world — a catalogue lists over 4,000 letters — and he published hitherto unprinted writings of Linnæus. Thus in 1811 Linné's remarkable diary of his Lappland journey appeared in an English translation — it was not made available in Swedish until 1888. A selection from Linné's correspondence in two volumes followed in 1821.

Apart from this, Smith was an industrious botanical writer. Among his works are the large, richly illustrated books *English Botany*, *Flora Britannica*, and *Flora Græca*, as well as smaller botanical handbooks.

When Smith died, his collections were offered by his widow to the Linnean Society, who acquired them for a sum of 3,000 guineas. For more than a hundred years, therefore, the Linnean Society has had the care of this priceless inheritance, and of the manner in which this trust has been fulfilled there can only be one opinion. Everything possible has been done to preserve these treasures from moth and decay— not forgetting London's harmful coal-dust and smoke.

In the Society's magnificent meeting-room, which by the way is adorned with portraits of Linnæus and many of the men who have made important contributions to the work of the Society, Charles Darwin among others, a whole wall is taken up by the cupboards of dark mahogany in which the Linnean collections are kept. Here, first and foremost, is Linné's herbarium. For a long time this was preserved in the simple deal cupboards designed by its original owner. The plants are glued on to sheets of good-quality paper. In most cases there is just the name of the species written on the front, and miscellaneous notes about origin etc. on the back. On the folio sheets enclosing each genus is written the name of the genus, all in Linné's own hand. The plants are, on the whole, amazingly well preserved.

Here, too, are Linné's butterfly collection, his fish collection (which in accordance with the method then in use is mounted with glue in the same way as the plants), and his collection of shells. The mineral collection has long since been scattered. It was sold by Smith when he removed from London in 1796 and went back to live in his home town, Norwich.

Linné's library, which occupies a whole cupboard on its own, contains, among other things, his own works, inter-leaved and furnished with numerous additions which often make them the equivalent of manuscripts. The letter collection comprises 19 bulky folio volumes bound in shagreen, containing about 3,000 letters. Finally, the manuscripts, consisting of about 20 bound volumes and as many box-files, contain the notes made by Linnæus himself from the time of his earliest scientific studies at Växjö Grammar-School up to the last years of his life.

It is a strange feeling to stand in this room on foreign soil where so much of the life's work of a great Swedish man is collected. If at first one feels sad because all this has not found a lasting home in a Swedish institution, and slightly bitter against those who were to blame for such neglect, on second thoughts one realizes that a much worse fate might easily have overtaken the collections. As late as 1936, in England of all places, it was possible for a part of the great Newton's manuscripts to be sold by public auction and dispersed for ever. Who can be sure that the same fate might not have befallen Linné's collections if they had remained here in Sweden? And another point: these collections, made accessible in a cosmopolitan city and scientific centre such as London, have been of untold importance to Linné's international renown. Sweden owes an ineffaceable debt of gratitude to the Linnean Society for the reverence with which it has adminis-tered and cared for its priceless possession.

There is not much that can be added to this account. It is, however, worth remarking that the above-mentioned selection of Linné's correspondence — *A Selection of the Correspondence of Linnæus and other Naturalists, from the original Manuscripts, by Sir James Edward Smith, London* 1821 — is made up of two large volumes and is a goldmine for the study of the history of eighteenth-century Europe's natural-scientific learning. The first comprehensive biography of Linnæus, in German, was published in 1792 by D. H. Stöver: *Leben des Ritters Carl von Linné*. It appeared in an English translation by Joseph Trapp two years later, *The Life of Sir Charles Linnæus, London* 1794, in a magnificent volume. But the English public was already familiar with Linnæus and his life's work. Here are a few lines, chosen at random from among many possible examples, from *Travels into Poland, Russia, Sweden and Denmark, by William Coxe, London* 1787:

The botanical garden of Upsala, to which place I had the pleasure of being accompanied by the son of Linnæus, is small, but laid out with judgment; and the collection of plants, particularly exotics, is numerous. I could not avoid regarding with enthusiasm this spot of ground, rendered celebrated by the residence of Linnæus; of whom it may be said, without exaggeration, that, in the natural history of the globe, he left nothing unexplored.

A somewhat comprehensive biography follows, which Coxe brings to a close with the following words:

The name of Linnæus may be classed amongst those of Newton, Boyle, Locke, Haller, Euler, and other great philosophers, who were friends to religion: he always testified in his conversations, writings, and actions, the highest reverence for the Supreme Being; and was so strongly impressed with the idea of omnipresence, that he wrote over the door of his library: *Innocui vivite, numen adest.*

The great merits of Linnæus, as a naturalist, are to be estimated from the rude state in which he found all the branches of natural history, and the perfection to which he carried them; in drawing order from confusion, and perspicuity from darkness: his understanding, comprehensive, yet accurate, was capable of combining and arranging an almost infinite variety of objects; which the magnitude of the greatest could not fatigue, nor the insignificance of the smallest elude. The mere catalogue of his works would make an ordinary pamphlet; and it would require no small volume to trace even the outlines of his system, now distinguished by the appellation of Linnean, which new methodized and reformed the whole compass of natural history. In these extensive and various pursuits, we know not which to admire most; his intimate knowledge; his fertility of invention; his indefatigable industry; his scientific arrangement; or that wonderful exactness in discriminating, where the minutest shades of difference are scarcely perceptible.

Goethe wrote in 1817: 'After Shakespeare and Spinoza, it is Linnæus who has had the greatest influence on me.' There is, admittedly, no equivalent statement by any great English writer; but from Gilbert White onwards there flows through English literature a mighty stream which is closely

related to what may be called the Linnean spirit. And finally,
what is most deeply characteristic of Linnæus is the union of
keen observation and contemplation,

> to look on Nature with a humble heart,
> self-question where it did not understand,
> and with a superstitious eye of love.

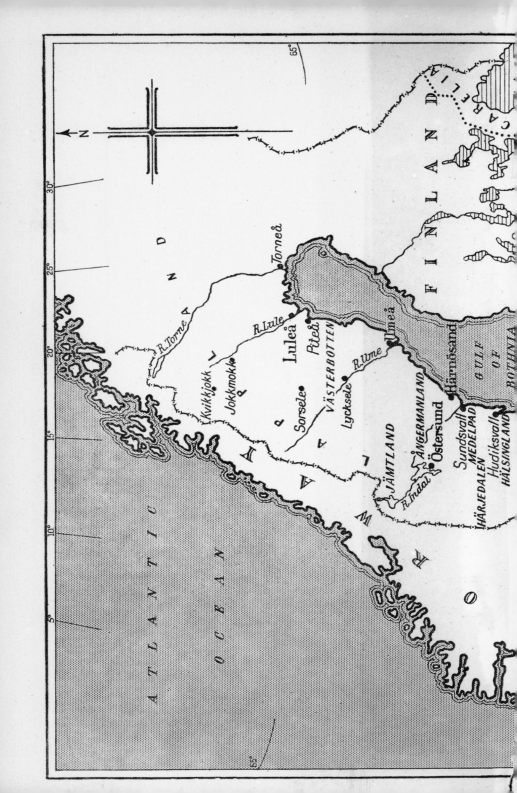